Brave Elizabeth

By Sheila Ingle
Illustrated by John Ingle

ISBN: 978-0-9912277-0-9

First printing, 2013
Second printing: April 2015
Third Printing: November 2017

Editor: Merianna Harrelson
Content Editor: Dr. Chris Swager
Cover Design: John Ingle

HARRELSON PRESS
PUBLISHING

For John

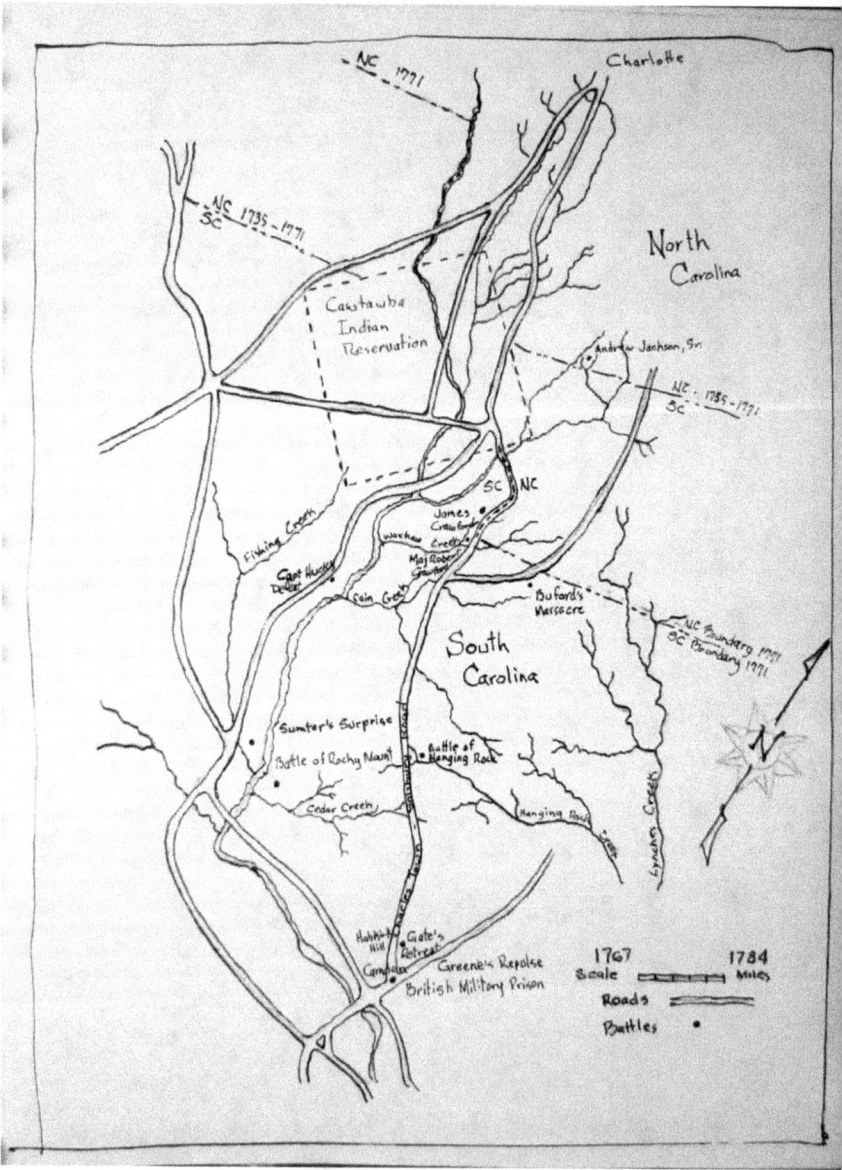

Andrew Jackson, Sr.
March, 1767

Unexpectedly sliding to his knee, Andrew Jackson winced when he lost his balance on the slippery layer of sleet over the snow. The thirty-year-old gingerly positioned both feet under him once again and chuckled at his clumsiness.

"An old man just like my da, I am becoming," he muttered, with a shake of his head.

Turning toward the pine trees, he saw how the eastern sun struck the crystals of sleet on the ground with flashing rays. Even the needles on those pines were glimmering from the frost. The surrounding beauty was treacherous. He rapidly blinked his eyes and shaded his face before striding forward. The gusty wind stung his face, and its blast seeped through his great coat. Today's March winds outdid the earlier winter's blusters, and spring's appearance was hidden in this landscape.

The icy ground and frigid temperature were just more tests to overcome; he had a task to complete. The woodpile was low, and more wood to chase the chill out of their cabin would be a necessity tonight. Andrew Jackson had to shorten the tree sections he had cut yesterday into smaller pieces to fit the fireplace. Bundled with extra clothing and two scarves wrapped around his face against the biting winds, he continued his walk toward the stand of pine trees nearby.

He stopped once again to survey his plot of land in the Waxhaws of Upcountry Carolina. While living in Boneybefore in Antrim, Ireland, he could only dream of owning land. He was a tenant farmer in Ireland, and most of his profits went monthly to the landlord. There were times when he almost went back to work for his father as a linen weaver, because of the everyday, wearying toil.

But now, Andrew never got over the satisfaction of seeing and smelling vegetables from his garden stewing in a pot hanging on the crane over his hearth. He whispered an early prayer of thanks for tonight's meal.

Andrew saw how Elizabeth's family had prospered in America. In the five years since he had settled here, James Crawford, the husband of Elizabeth's sister, Jane, had built a large house that was enough for company. His livelihood was in the crops that he had raised.

Looking at his own fields in the distance, Andrew knew additional trees would have to be cut down before spring planting. This year he would plant more corn because their family was growing.

Elizabeth was expecting their third child any day now. Andrew yearned for his land here on Ligget's Branch to bring about a fine living for his family.

Elizabeth's sisters and their husbands had helped them get started when they arrived in this new country, and Andrew was grateful. That was one of the reasons that he had decided to join the congregation at Waxhaw Meeting House, rather than attending the Sugar Creek Meeting House closer to his home. The twelve-mile trek on Sundays was not an inconvenience. Family was important to all Scotch- Irish, and Andrew was no exception. Spending time together cemented the bond of closeness between them, and Andrew knew he would always be able to depend on her family. He also wanted them to know that his loyalty and help was guaranteed.

Continuing to mull over their help as he staggered a bit again, Andrew remembered all the meals the sisters had happily delivered to them. Just like Elizabeth, their blue eyes danced with excitement when they were together. Even though their help wasn't a necessity now, the sisters continued to find reasons to enjoy each other's company.

Besides sharing seed for their first crops, the men had worked alongside him to raise their cabin. Even their pastor, Reverend William Richardson, joined the work crew. They all helped cut trees for the barn and worked vigorously with Andrew until both structures were sturdy and weather resistant.

Rather than the traditional, thatched home like they had in Ireland, they now lived in a one-room cabin, fashioned from their own trees. Burning logs for cooking and heating, rather than peat, was another improvement. Even though there was a dirt floor, Elizabeth had woven rugs whose colors warmed up the room.

Elizabeth's family divided their own cows, sheep, pigs, and chickens to give these new immigrants a start with the farm animals. Andrew's cow would calve soon, and it looked like she would have twins. Even though the winter of 1767 had been rough, all the animals were still healthy. Now it was time for him to prove himself as the head of his household and take care of his own family.

Andrew wished his brother Hugh was here to enjoy time with his namesake.

Yesterday had been a fair-weather day, and Andrew had mended fences with his oldest son, Hugh. Hugh's job was to hand his papa the nails. Andrew was proud of the four-year-old; the boy truly wanted to help with the chores.

Often Andrew looked around and saw the youngster stretching hard to closely follow his papa; the child even tried to walk exactly in his father's footsteps. Hugh would concentrate as he made giant steps behind him. Andrew realized what a responsibility he had to be a good model for both his sons. He prayed his example would always be worthy of following.

Once again, Andrew's boots slipped and slid on

the frozen red clay. He almost fell headlong into a pile of leaves and pine needles.

Flinging his ax steadied him from completely losing his balance.

"Egad!" Andrew hollered as he straightened himself to a standing position. "Seems like the wee folk are playing their tricks on me today!"

Frowning at his own carelessness, he warily walked to pick up his ax. The solitary woodpile was in plain sight of the log cabin, and he had other chores to tend to that morning. There was no time for further distraction in this day. He marched to his task.

Pushing the smaller log off the wider one with his foot, Andrew bent down, grabbed the shorter branches, and yanked the larger piece with all his might. Andrew could see that this was not going to be much of a tug-of-war. The log was stuck, but one more jerk would pull it free. Thinking about the warm fire that would keep their home cozy all night with this one log, once more he pulled. Inch by inch, the log followed Andrew's hands; he steadily hauled it out from under the pile.

As he sweated from the exertion of pulling, he felt his efforts strain the muscles of his arms, and then in his legs. Concentrating on his task, he didn't realize his mouth was clenched. His whole body and mind were deliberately focused on the chore.

With one final, backward lurch of his whole body, the log was freed.

Andrew screamed in pain and grabbed his stomach. The spot that had been bothering him was pulling and jabbing again. Even though he had been successful with the tree section, there was now a lingering pain at the top of his leg to deal with.

Turning from the woodpile and picking up his ax, his gait was now hesitant and painful, but he gritted his teeth and kept stepping. Each stumble was now agony, but his fierce determination moved him forward. Every few feet, Andrew gulped to catch his breath. The stabs of pain were now constant, and perspiration dripped down his face from his exertions. His brown eyes became glazed over with throbbing torture. The slippery ground was no concern now; Andrew's single-minded focus was to reach his wife, Elizabeth. She would know what to do.

As he finally stepped onto their porch, Andrew panted for breath to speak. Only one, forced word escaped his lips, "Elizabeth!"

Within seconds, she flung open the door. Seeing Andrew's stooped frame, as he clutched his stomach, she knew something dreadful had happened.

"Andrew, I'm here!" she screamed.

He could not speak. Draping his arm over her shoulders, she struggled to both keep her balance and support his weight. Elizabeth was much shorter than Andrew, but his bent over stance made it easier for them to steady each other.

Her cap fell off in her dash, and red hair tumbled down past her shoulders. Except for pushing the tendrils out of her eyes, she didn't notice the immediate disarray, nor stopped to shut the door, so the cold winter wind whirled the couple into the cabin.

Their two sons, Hugh and Robert, scattered their blocks and ran to their parents.

"Papa, I can help you walk. I am strong as a bear, Papa! You told me that just yesterday," the four-year-old Hugh exclaimed.

The boy bounced beside his parents, not really knowing what to do or how to help.

It was only a few more steps to the bed. Taking off his wet boots and great coat, Elizabeth carefully helped Andrew to lie down. His wrinkled brow and harsh breathing told her the pain level was intense.

Andrew complained little about the daily hurts and bruises that went along with the hard work of clearing land and hanging on to civilization in the middle of a forest. Without taking time to check out any injuries, he would shrug his shoulders, give a wink, and go onto the next task.

Now, his eyes were tightly shut, as if to shut out the pain.

Desperately, Elizabeth sought answers from her husband. "Andrew! Can you hear me? Tell me, darling, what happened?"

Andrew opened his eyes, seeking her face, and barely shook his head.

Andrew's tricorn had fallen off his head when he came in the door, and two-year-old Robert picked it up. Then, the child toddled across the room and carefully stood on his tiptoes to place the hat on the table. Nodding his head as if he knew he had helped, Robert went back to his blocks.

Hugh stood at the foot of the bed, patting his papa's feet; he was old enough to recognize that his papa was in pain. He knew what a comfort his mama's patting was when he was hurt, so he hoped he could do some good for his hurt father. The boy kept looking from one parent to another with many questions in his eyes. Hugh wanted his papa to open his eyes, wink, and get off the bed, and he didn't understand what the delay was.

By now Andrew's mouth was shut tight, and Elizabeth knew that his furrowed brow was a mask for the agony he was feeling, He didn't want to scare her or his sons, so he was silent. She knew what an effort it was for him to be quiet. His hands were clamped together over a spot on his stomach, as if he was trying to hold it in. Sometimes, he grabbed both his hands and pushed, trying to shove the pain away.

6

Elizabeth wanted to know what had happened, so she would understand how to help. At this point, she recognized he couldn't answer questions. Knowing in her heart that a tranquil countenance, not a panicked one, was what Andrew and her boys needed to see, Elizabeth took a deep breath and sat down beside him on the bed.

Suddenly noticing the bitter weather was invading her home, Elizabeth spoke to Hugh. "Son, shut the door, or we'll all be sick."

A loud groan escaped Andrew's lips, and he lapsed into a coma before Elizabeth could speak again. She dropped to her knees beside the bed and nestled his hands in her own. Shutting her eyes, she earnestly prayed.

"Father in Heaven, have mercy on Andrew. He is hurt, and I don't know what to do. He is in pain, and he can't stand it. Reach out your Mighty Arm of healing, and touch my Andrew   "

Deep sobs halted her prayers, and weeping filled their log cabin home, Hugh and Robert both crawled into their mama's lap for comfort.

Elizabeth Jackson would do what she had to do.

A Grieving Widow
March, 1767

The flurries were falling faster now, and it softly blanketed the ground and the wagon trail leading away from the meeting house.

The children were catching countless flakes in their mouths and trying to make snowballs. Some were flat on their backs, wildly moving arms and legs to create angels. Seeing how the cold air crafted their breath into fog led to contests of blowing on each other. Squeals of joy and excitement filled the air. Just like the snowflakes, their exuberance crowded the courtyard.

Elizabeth Jackson, holding the toddler Robert in her arms, stood on the porch of Waxhaw Meeting House and watched her oldest son, Hugh, who was reveling in all the fun. Squealing with excitement and wiggling to get down, Robert stretched out his hands to join the excitement. His mother carefully put his feet on the ground. Elizabeth didn't want to lose her own footing on the icy steps; she barely trusted her stability in her late pregnancy.

Two-year-old Robert carefully made the short journey to Hugh's side and cried, " 'now! 'now! Want 'now!"

Ever the older brother, Hugh turned Robert's hands palm-up, so he could catch the snowflakes. As they fell through Robert's hands, he gleefully called, "My 'now! See my 'now!"

Her children's fun brought a smile to the new widow's face, but it didn't reach her eyes or her heart. Trying not to let her grief overwhelm her again, Elizabeth wrapped her wool cape around herself and pulled the hood tighter around her chin. Her fingerless gloves did little for her fingers, but boots kept her feet warm. Andrew had always insisted that each member of his family have a sturdy pair of shoes for the winter season.

Four of Elizabeth's sisters Jane, Margaret, Sarah, and Grace, stood close to her. Nancy Richardson, the minister's wife and Elizabeth's best friend, replaced the dark blue scarf around her neck. The scarf had fallen when Robert was put down, and Elizabeth grabbed its warmth with both hands. It was Andrew's scarf; Elizabeth had tightly held it during the funeral service.

Elizabeth turned to Nancy and her sisters with a puzzled face. "What am I going to do now?"

Gulping for breath, she covered her face with his scarf. The women gathered closer to surround Elizabeth with love and concern.

Pushing in between their skirts to get to his mamma, Robert held up a handful of snow to Elizabeth. As it dripped through his chubby fingers, his grin spread from ear to ear.

" 'now fwakes, Mama!"

Then he turned and bounded off to frolic with his friends.

As Elizabeth took her son's melting present, Nancy quickly spoke, "I believe this is the answer to your question, Elizabeth. Just like you always have, you will just continue to do the next thing, whatever it is. Today, you accepted a gift of snow."

The other women nodded their heads in agreement. It was hard to hope for the future because it was uncertain. Every ordinary day was a treasure.

Jane added, "That reminds me of the scripture Reverend Richardson read last Sunday about worrying about tomorrow. Aye, you are right, Nancy, we just need to do the next thing on today's list."

Soft talk and whispers were now the only sounds on the porch. They waited for Elizabeth to give them a sign that she was ready to leave the meeting house. It was obvious that she was woolgathering, even though her blue eyes watched her children.

*****

In her daydream, Elizabeth was back in Ireland to a happier time.

It was a warm, summer day when Andrew's brother Sam came by their farm for a visit. The brothers were glad to see one another and heartily pounded each other on the back. Sam was a sailor, and his visits back to family were infrequent. That evening, he regaled them with his latest stories of all the exotic places he had been.

As a common sailor, not an officer, Sam's privileges were few. No matter his position onboard, his excitement over his adventures was contagious. Andrew was spellbound, and he questioned his brother about life at sea. Sam's enthusiasm never wavered, even though he was honest about both the dangers and the hardship. Listening to his brother's honesty about the perils they contended with like attacks by pirates on each voyage and the scarcity of food, Andrew still caught Sam's spirit and wanderlust.

For days after Sam's visit, Andrew mulled over the yarns he had heard. Elizabeth noticed more silences in the evenings. Rather than worrying about their next month's rent or the lack of rain, Andrew quietly packed and smoked his pipe.

Andrew started to second-guess leaving the weaving business, and every night weighed his options with Elizabeth. With his decision to tenant farm, Andrew believed he could provide a more stable life for his family. But the weather had not cooperated for two seasons, and poor crops were the result. Selling the Irish

10

linen that Elizabeth spun and wove in front of their hearth only paid for the rent of the land and house. She was known for the quality of her cloth, and there was always a demand for it. They even raised their own flax, but although the demand was high, there was still never enough money.

Then one day, Andrew started talking and speculating about a move to the Carolinas. Each night, the young couple weighed the options of a better life for their children if they migrated.

Just a few weeks later, Andrew's brother, Hugh Jackson, returned from his duties as a soldier in His Majesty' service. His regiment had moved from Quebec to Virginia to the Waxhaws, and the New World was a daily marvel to him. Besides the plentiful game and fish, the lush soil, and the abundant forests, Hugh met content families who were thriving. Elizabeth remembered listening to Hugh's enthusiasm.

One day when she was rocking baby Robert, it dawned on her that she had four sisters to reunite with in the Waxhaws

Hugh recounted a tale about hunting with a tribe of Indians called the Catawbas. Even though his regiment had fought against another Indian tribe called the Cherokees, Hugh was obviously taken with the land and its people.

He was anxious to return, and Andrew was ready to leave with him that very day. The two brothers immediately started to plan this family undertaking. They both were impatient to start over; hope for a better life was across the Atlantic Ocean, not in Ireland. From that point on, Elizabeth was eager to pack and leave.

By selling their few pieces of furniture, two horses, one cow, a small herd of sheep, and a few chickens, Andrew had the required money to buy their tickets. He paid 3 pounds 10 shillings for each of their tickets, and he hoped enough remained to buy land near Elizabeth's family.

A slight smile came to Elizabeth's face as she remembered the morning they sailed. Poor Hugh and his wife stood on the wharf and waved good-bye; she refused to leave Ireland. His woebegone expression was in direct contrast to his wife's broad smile.

Hugh had coaxed and even bribed her with promises of returning to Ireland if she was unhappy. Nothing had changed her mind, so Andrew, Elizabeth, and their two children put out to sea without them. Elizabeth's smile was also wide; she was overjoyed about moving closer to her sisters.

It was 1765, and there was only the Atlantic Ocean to cross for the Jackson family to settle down in a new home.

Leaving from the port of Larne, the eight-week voyage was long on *The Prince of Wales* to Charleston in Carolinas, but uneventful. The storms were scary, but the gales did little damage to the sails or the ship. There was no variety in the regular fare of bread, potatoes, and sometimes salted beef. Every inch of the ship was crowded with people. Daily, the thankful adults prayed for the continued boredom that was unmixed with excitement.

After the Jacksons landed, it was only a few days before they started on the land trek of their journey. Weeks of traveling with six- month-old Robert and two-year-old Hugh in that Conestoga wagon to reach the Waxhaws was taxing.

A large, covered wagon was the only option for a family. At a rate of about fifteen miles a day, the team of six horses pulled the four- wheeled wagon through rivers and across the well-worn paths of those who went before them. Food for the journey was contained in roped- down boxes and baskets. Cords kept the linen chest and the firkins filled with necessaries. A feed box for the horses was strapped to the back of the wagon, and water barrels were attached to the side. The wagon was like a home on wheels.

Hugh would point at the wagon and holler, "Boat! Boat!" No matter how many times Elizabeth or Andrew corrected Hugh, the child was convinced the wagon was a boat. As Andrew came back one day from hunting, he walked up an embankment toward the camp. Just before he climbed over the rise, he caught a glimpse of their wagon home. He finally realized the image that Hugh kept seeing; the wagon did resemble a boat. The floors of the wagon curved upward just like the stem and stern of a ship, and the canvas top looked like the sails on the ship. From that day forward, the parents nodded at Hugh whenever he made his declaration.

*****

"Mama! Mama!" Robert's cries broke into Elizabeth's reverie.

Robert had tumbled one too many times. He needed his mama.

As Elizabeth picked him up and wiped the tears and melting snow off his face, she wondered which one of her boys would inherit the adventurous spirit and fire of her husband.

The husbands of Elizabeth's sisters and the other men from the congregation were huddled together in the yard close to the wagons and horses. Nodding and watching the antics of the children brought back memories of their own childhoods, and they swapped tales. Because of the wind and the snow, it was hard to keep their clay pipes lit, but they continued to struggle. Cupping their hands was only effective for a few seconds. Peppered with the fallen and melting flakes,

13

their cloaks and hunting shirts dripped. Even their beaver and wool felt hats showed the results of weather's sting. They stamped their feet to keep them warm; standing still could bring on frostbite.

At long last, the men were idle, because their work in the graveyard was completed.

James Crawford, Jane's husband, was the last to join the tight knot of men. Carrying his shovel, he pitched it into the back of his wagon, rather than heaving it into the trees like he wanted to. His expression showed the frustration and fatigue of the past couple of days.

"It's done then?" asked Reverend William Richardson, the ten- year pastor of the Waxhaws congregation.

"The ground is all smoothed out, Reverend, and we appreciate your words of comfort today. We are blessed to have you as our church leader."

The others nodded their agreement.

"I will miss Andrew Jackson," he continued. "He was a hard worker and a good man. Even though the red clay of his land was hard to grow crops in, he made a living for his family."

Margaret's husband, George McKemey, added, "I still don't understand how his accident happened. He was always careful and methodical when working. Mayhap, he was overbalanced, and the log abruptly slipped out of his hands."

"His land was ten miles off the post road and isolated a bit from the rest of us, but he saw to it that Elizabeth saw her sisters on a regular basis. Sarah says often the sisters agree that their time spent together is like a gift." Sam Leslie noted.

A snowball hit James' arm, and the men turned to the children's games once again. It was good to see them having fun on this heartrending day.

Mr. O'Donnell constructed a fine box for

Andrew from that cherry tree on his property," observed George. "He has a steady hand for building, and that fine wood was stacked in his barn. When his daughter died last year of whooping cough, he split the boards then. . . a generous man to our Elizabeth."

The men nodded in agreement.

"I know we will all miss Andrew; he is the first of our generation to die. We will need to stand in the gap to help Elizabeth, her boys, and the new babe," said James Crow, Grace's husband.

"Jane and I have been talking about that," replied James Crawford. "Jane has not fully recovered from that lung disease she had last winter. Some days she can't even get out of bed, and she dearly wants Elizabeth to come live with us. We need help, and the two have always been close. Jane is going to talk with her today. I sure hope Elizabeth will see it as a good thing to do."

On the porch, Elizabeth again pushed back the agonizing pain of loss. She was trying not to panic from the nightmare that had invaded her life. She heard someone say her name and turned to the strained face of her sister Jane.

"I need you, Elizabeth. Will you and the boys come home with James and me?"

The simple request touched Elizabeth's heart. She nodded her head.

The Weaver's Daughter
1769

  The Crawford home, built on a knoll close to the post road seven years before, was spacious. The keeping room and a sizable bedroom were on the first level. There was a large, undivided, second floor room where the children slept. It was a roomy house that welcomed and entertained travelers. The sisters, Jane and Elizabeth, were known for their hospitality.

  Every night, the Crawfords and Jacksons gathered together to sing; it was a family tradition brought from Ireland. Before the children ever learned the words of any of the songs, they joined in by humming or banging wooden spoons on the floor.

  Tonight, as the eleven children clapped, James positioned the fiddle under his chin once again. He bent his head to the right, and the strains introduced another tune known to them all. It was *The Bog Down in the Valley-o*:

Ho, ro, the rattlin' bog,
The bog down in the valley-o,
Ho, ro, the rattlin' bog,
The bog down in the valley-o.

Now in that bog there was a tree,
A rare tree and a rattlin' tree,
And the tree in the bog,
And the bog down in the valley-o.

Ho, ro, the rattlin' bog,
The bog down in the valley-o.
Ho, ro, the rattlin' bog,
The bog down in the valley-o.

Now on that tree there was a branch,
A rare branch and a rattlin' branch,
And the branch on the tree,
And the bog down in the valley-o.

Ho, ro, the rattlin' bog,
The bog down in the valley-o.
Ho, ro, the rattlin' bog,
The bog down in the valley-o.

Now on that branch there was a limb,
A rare limb and a rattlin' limb,
And the limb on the branch,
And the branch on the tree,
And the tree in the bog,
And the bog down in the valley-o.

Ho, ro, the rattlin' bog,
The bog down in the valley-o.
Ho, ro, the rattlin' bog,
The bog down in the valley-o.

Now on that limb there was a nest,
A rare nest and a rattlin' nest,
And the nest on the limb,
And the limb on the branch,
And the branch on the tree,
And the tree in the bog,
And the bog down in the valley-o.

Ho, ro, the rattlin' bog,
The bog down in the valley-o.
Ho, ro, the rattlin' bog,
The bog down in the valley-o.

17

Now in that nest there was a bird,
A rare bird and a rattlin' bird,
And the bird in the nest,
And the nest on the limb,
And the limb on the branch,
And the branch on the tree,
And the tree in the bog,
And the bog down in the valley-o.

Ho, ro, the rattlin' bog,
The bog down in the valley-o.
Ho, ro, the rattlin' bog,
The bog down in the valley-o.

Now on that bird there was a feather,
A rare feather and a rattlin' feather,
And the feather on the bird,
And the bird in the nest,
And the nest on the limb,
And the limb on the branch,
And the branch on the tree,
And the tree in the bog,
And the bog down in the valley-o.

Ho, ro, the rattlin' bog,
The bog down in the valley-o.
Ho, ro, the rattlin' bog,
The bog down in the valley-o.

Now on that feather there was a bug,
A rare bug and a rattlin' bug,
And the bug on the feather,
And the feather on the bird,
And the bird in the nest,
And the nest on the limb,

And the limb on the branch,
And the branch on the tree,
And the tree in the bog,
And the bog down in the valley-o.

Ho, ro, the rattlin' bog,
The bog down in the valley-o.
Ho, ro, the rattlin' bog,
The bog down in the valley-o.

By the end of the last chorus, the singing, clapping, stomping, and dancing raised a clamor that was hard to stop. The dogs added to the uproar with their howling. All the curious night animals had long since skulked away from the hullabaloo created by the Jackson and Crawford families.

As Andy, named after his father Andrew Jackson, fell down in a heap from the exertion, his four-year-old brother Robert gasped, "More! More singing!"

Other childish voices quickly joined him, but James shook his head and placed his fiddle and bow across his knees. His signals were pointed and clear to all in the room: it was bedtime.

Smiling at the room full of worn-out, but keyed-up, children, Elizabeth stood from her chair and motioned toward the stairs. Even though her two youngest boys were limp, she helped Andy and Robert to stand with her firm support. With a hug and a quick kiss, she gently guided them toward the staircase.

Noisy with words and shoves, the keeping room emptied. As the oldest, Thomas Crawford brushed past Elizabeth on his way to be first. Pushing and jostling each other, his brothers James and Alexander, weren't far behind.

"I won!" shouted Alexander, as he lunged past his brother at the top of the stairs and sprawled on the floorboards. Scuffling sounds identified James' response to his brother's win.

After his hug from Elizabeth, Hugh Jackson dashed to join his cousins' race to the loft. The thuds of their feet and intentional falls against each other and the walls were unusually feverish.

Clapping her hands over her ears, the nervous, two-year- old Margaret and four-year- old Elizabeth deliberately slowed their paces. Just as Margaret lost her balance, her older sister Jennie picked her up and rescued her. Martha and Mary scooped up Elizabeth in a chair made by their arms, so she was safely on her way.

With their mother Jane already in bed for the evening because of her illness, Elizabeth hugged and kissed her eight Crawford nieces and nephews as they walked was one ritual that no one ever missed at the end of the day. Elizabeth and Jane's mother had modeled these end-of- the-day love touches when they were growing up, and the sisters wanted to pass it on to their own children.

The loft was the ideal sleeping space for the children. The boys gathered together on one side, and the girls on the other. If anyone forgot the imaginary line down the middle of the room, numerous voices hollered quick reminders.

The beds were close together, but Elizabeth had woven a small rug for each child. Different in colors and sizes, the rugs identified an individual's space. Pushing fights and angry words often rang out if someone dared to touch another's rug. The older children teased the younger ones by hiding theirs or holding them out-of-reach. Meltdowns or running for adult intervention were the outcomes for these diversions, but the escapades were soon forgotten.

They were normal children who fussed, fought and picked on each other, but they tended to get along most days.

Listening to the loud whispers from upstairs as they readied themselves for bed, Elizabeth banked the fire in the hearth.

She turned at James' voice.

"Elizabeth, I trust you have everything you need? That is a passel of lads and lassies you tend to everyday. In truth, we are beholden to you. You love on our children same as your own and switch them all equally. It's a mystery to me how you keep all of us on the straight and narrow as well as look after my Jane, too."

"Oh, James, you and Jane took me in when I didn't know what to do or where to go. She and I have ever been close, and I relish my days with her now. Being useful to someone has always brought me pleasure. I think she enjoys telling me how to do things, while making me laugh at the same time. Mayhap that just comes from being my older sister."

James chuckled at the thought that his wife might be a tad bossy but didn't comment. He nodded good night and went on to bed.

Elizabeth tugged her small rocker closer to the light and pulled her Bible from one of her pockets. Wrapped in a checkered cloth, it was her prized possession. Her favorite verses were in the Psalms. Tonight, she sought Psalm 119:105. "Thy Word is a Lamp unto my feet and a light unto my path."

As she read silently, her calloused fingers lightly rubbed the page. Closing the cover, she prayed for her little family and her extended family. Being without a husband in this wilderness was difficult, and she missed Andrew. Daily she fought the grief that she felt would never go away. Elizabeth thanked God for His provision of James and his godly influence on her three sons. James was a blessing to all of them, and she didn't take his protection lightly.

Then she prayed for this new country and its struggles with England. New taxes over the past several years had maddened many. All of Elizabeth's family were outraged by the burdens the new levies would drain from their home budgets. The main reason the Scotch-Irish had left Ireland was to get away from both the exorbitant, English tariffs and religious discrimination. Elizabeth concluded her prayer by asking for wisdom for the colonies' leaders to know the path Providence had for them.

As Elizabeth rose, she heard the faint sounds of "Ho, ro, the rattlin' bog, The bog down in the valley-o." Recognizing the garbled voice of Andy, she was sure he was almost asleep and decided not to chastise him.

Picking up her candlestick from the table, Elizabeth sought her own sleep in the small, but cozy, bedroom James had built just for her. He had attached it to the house behind the fireplace. She was grateful for her own space.

*****

"Boys, 'tis time to leave the marbles for now. You can go back to playing later. Your help is needed," called Elizabeth the next morning.

Hugh, Robert, and Andy all took one more turn before they slowly stood and meandered toward the porch. To prolong the inevitable, Hugh and Robert walked toe-to-toe. Andy was just beginning to be taught chores, and he was curious about the newness of it all. Following his brothers, his pace was not far behind them.

Playtime never lasted long enough on this homestead, but work could be fun.

The older Crawford boys were helping James in

the field. They were cleaning up the weeds from the day before. When the young plants were five inches tall, the youngest children weeded the crop. Because their feet were small and the plants were planted closely together, the barefoot children would not hurt the plants. Yesterday had been the day for those bottom-land flax fields to be cleared, and the children had relished their assignments. Laughter and squeals rang like bells; stomping the weeds was a game.

This morning, Jane was resting, so Elizabeth had assigned everyone else an outside job. Soon many tasks were going on in a small place making porch life lively. Martha was churning butter, and Jennie was spinning. The five youngest children, including the three Jackson brothers, had the chore of carding wool. All work was completed in stages; it took days to complete most chores.

For over a week, they had been working with the wool. Yesterday, the last of the fleece was washed in soapy water in large pots. The fire under the pots was fed with sticks to keep the water hot. Large wooden paddles were used to push and pull the wool out of the water. The wool was placed on bushes or the grass to dry. When the water became dirty, it was thrown out, and the work continued.

"It took all day for the wool to dry on the bushes. Usually only a few hours in the sun will have it warm and dry, but not yesterday," observed Jennie.

Elizabeth replied, "Perchance those clouds in the morning slowed down the drying."

Because Jennie had become a natural spinner, she wasn't aware of the hand, eye, and foot coordination that was involved. Turning the wheel several times quickly with her right hand, she swung her left hand to the right and walked forward. Onto the spindle, the yarn was wound. Then she started the identical process over by turning the wheel with her right hand while walking backward.

Jennie nodded while she worked. "I love rubbing the yellow, sticky mess on my hands and face. Even after boiling in that hot water, there is always a little left in the strands of the wool after it dries."

Martha chimed in, "It's curious the way the wool isn't as soft after it's washed."

"Girls, we need to put that soft substance from the sheep in the soap when we make it next time. Mayhap, it will help our skin to stay softer. It appears I am the one learning from you today," smiled Elizabeth.

Carding was a tedious task that cleaned and straightened the fibers all at one time. The wool was placed on the teeth of each card, and then one card was pulled across the other one. Any dirt or straw fell to the ground, and the fibers were straightened for spinning.

Andy was still learning, and his hands were too small to hold two cards at the same time. Hugh put his younger brother to work pulling small handfuls of wool out of the basket. Then Andy laid the thick, curly wool on Hugh and Robert's cards.

"Mama, the sheep look sad without their wool," remarked Hugh. "They hang their heads. Can't we let them keep their wool?"

"Oh, Hugh, they would truly be sad if we didn't shear them. Their wool would be too heavy for them to walk, and they would be very hot during the summer," explained Elizabeth. "We need the wool to make our clothes, and the sheep will grow more wool quite soon."

Glancing up at her oldest, she noticed his short breeches. Some of his clothes could be passed down, but not all. Looking around at short dresses and breeches on the other children made her spin faster.

"All of you have grown taller over the winter, and this wool thread is precisely what I need. Besides if

24

we don't spin thread to weave, we won't have any material.

I can't do it without all of you to help; it is too much work for one person. I am so proud of the way we can all work together and not depend on getting any fabric from another country!"

The children heard the pleasure in her voice and sat up straighter.

Within minutes of everyone starting their assigned tasks, the children began to clamor for a Jack tale. Elizabeth knew they would work longer with a wee bit of entertainment, so she started her storytelling. Since spinning was second nature to her, she could work without thinking.

"How about Jack and the beans, Mamma?" asked Robert.

"You always want to hear that story, Robert," Martha exclaimed. "Is there a new one, Aunt Elizabeth?" Elizabeth pondered for a moment and then started weaving a story together she remembered her grandfather telling.

Jack had worked hard for his master in England for several years, but one day he grew tired and lazy. He wanted to go home and see his father and mother.

His master gave Jack a lump of silver as big as the boy's head as payment for his work.

Jack started home immediately. The silver was heavy, and soon Jack grew tired. He sat down on the side of the road to rest. Looking down the road, he saw a man on a handsome horse riding toward him. The man sat upright in the saddle and held his head high. Jack had an idea.

Jack waved at the man to stop, and the rider did. The man saw the lump of silver, and he wanted it. Soon the man talked Jack into an exchange: Jack would get the handsome horse in return for the lump of silver. Jack immediately agreed.

Before Jack climbed on the horse, the owner told Jack to say, 'Git up' if he wanted to ride fast. Not too far down the road, Jack smiled and said, 'Git up.' The horse reared up, and Jack fell off.

Jack just sat there. Then he saw a man driving a cow in front of him. Jack got up and told the man he would swap the horse for the cow. The man was glad to oblige.

Wanting some milk to go with the bread he had brought with him, Jack tried to milk the cow. But the cow kicked him and jumped away.

Elizabeth's audience laughed at this word picture, and she continued.

Jack heard laughter behind him. It was a man with a pig tied by the hind leg. Jack decided he would like some pig meat to go with his bread, rather than milk. So he traded once again.

The pig wanted to go in another direction, and Jack couldn't control him. But luck was with Jack, because a man was walking up the road with a white goose under his arm. Jack traded once again. He knew the goose could lay an egg every day for his food, and the goose feathers could be sold. Jack was finally happy.

Jack neared a small village. He met a man working away with a grindstone.

He told Jack that he always had work because of the grinder.

Yet again, Jack swapped.

Happy with the stone on his back, Jack walked on. He grew tired and thirsty. He found a well and leaned over to see if he could see water. The stone fell off his back into the well.

Jack walked back to the road, sat down, and thought, "I have nothing to worry me and nothing to carry that will make me tired."

Happily, Jack ate his dried bread.

"Jack should have kept the horse, Mamma," said Hugh. "I like horses. I want a horse like Uncle James has."

"Me, too. I want a horse," shouted Robert.

Most of the time a Jack story made chores easier, and today's Jack story worked its magic on the carding task.

The Waxhaws Presbyterian Church
July, 1771

Waxhaws Presbyterian Church was formally organized in 1758. Shortly thereafter, the congregation called their first ordained minister, Reverend William Richardson.

For twelve years now, he had served as their minister after an unsuccessful and disheartening missionary experience to the Cherokees. Sometimes the memories of those difficult and futile days still brought sadness to his face. The Scotch-Irish often noted his remarkable piety and devotion to God, but the Indians had not responded to his messages.

After moving to the Waxhaws, he bought land and married Nancy Craighead, the daughter of another Presbyterian minister who served at nearby Sugar Creek Church. Nancy had been born in Virginia and brought up in a well-to-do home; she brought an extensive dowry of silver, linens, glassware, and furniture. She was hospitable and enjoyed visitors. Though William felt more comfortable in his study reading a book or his Bible, he also appreciated time with his congregation.

The church was the center of this religious community, and the Richardson's home was always open. Their two-story manse was a gathering place for the congregation because the couple hosted literary evenings on a regular basis.

Built near the Catawba River, it was superior to many homes in the community. Most families, though they owned their own land, had much smaller homes. Some were still living in one- room cabins.

Both children and adults filled it that warm July night in 1771.

The apple cider was sitting on the trestle table ready to be served. Fall was the season for apple picking, and none of the households wasted the tasty, picked fruit throughout the year. Women stored apples in their cellars and kitchens. After the harvest in October, the fruit was preserved in baskets or barrels and then covered with either hay or sand.

To get apples ready for drying, they were first peeled, cored, and quartered. They were dried outside on boards. Then, the apples were threaded on string and hung from the beams on the kitchen ceiling. Hanging them discouraged the mice from reveling in a private, apple- tasting party. For added protection from the rodent crooks, sometimes the women would also place the dried apples in cloth bags tightly closed with string.

Both Nancy and Elizabeth regularly used their apple presses to make cider from their stored apples; they were hoping to have enough to last until the next harvest was in.

Elizabeth had lined up all her pewter and wooden mugs and filled them with the cold cider. It had been made just three days before and stored in crocks in the nearby spring. This latest batch had been made from the small apples left in the cellar. The cool liquid was the ideal temperature for this warm night.

"I like your ginger cookies," said Nancy, as she nibbled on one of the thin, crispy sweets on the plate. "They snap and melt, almost simultaneously. Do you have a special secret ingredient? You know I am a collector of receipts."

"My mum's granny passed down this receipt. We Hutchinson girls memorized it at an early age, because we fancied their aroma, as well as their taste. Granny sold her gingersnaps at the market and always returned home with an empty basket, as well as jingling pockets. Both neighbors and strangers stood in line to buy her cookies. Many a time, I burned my tongue by not waiting 'til they cooled. There were even times we pretended we had a chill because ginger snaps were the cure-all for sneezes and sniffles. I believe Mum was privy to our games, but she still spoiled us by baking the cookies."

Smiling with thoughts of her mother and grandmother, Elizabeth continued.

"Mix two cups flour, a pinch of allspice, 1/2 teaspoon cinnamon, two tablespoons fresh ginger, and 1/2 teaspoon baking soda in a large bowl. Then, blend two tablespoons melted butter with 1/2 cup molasses and three tablespoons water in another bowl."

Before either woman could push the cat away, Nancy's spry old tabby unexpectedly jumped on the table and snatched a whole cookie. The cookie disappeared in one bite, and the crumbs on that mouser's whiskers quickly vanished, too. She paused to cast a haughty look toward the two women. Then, with a swish of her tail, the cat easily landed on the floor on all four paws. With her head held high, the bandit flounced out the kitchen door.

Startled by the quick theft and the crook's attitude, the women laughed.

"Indeed, one of these days, I am going to snatch that cat baldheaded! She has a mite too much boldness for me," declared Nancy.

Still chuckling, Elizabeth continued giving the receipt directions. "Knead and roll out the dough. Use any or all of your tin cookie cutters for the shapes you want. Bake the cookies only a few wee minutes in a very hot oven. Perchance that short baking time might be the secret to these crunchy cookies, Nancy," finished Elizabeth.

Nancy turned to Elizabeth to give her a hug.

"I'm most glad you are my neighbor, Elizabeth.

I don't know what I would do without you. Whether you are sharing a receipt or only sitting a spell with me, I prithee you will always be my friend."

"You are like a sister to me, Nancy, not just a friend," Elizabeth immediately replied. "These past four years have been powerful hard without my dear Andrew. Our three sons are a handful most times. You have always found time to listen to my doubts on nurturing them on the right paths."

Ever the good hostess, Nancy looked once more at the wooden trays and picked one up. "Mayhap it is time to serve our guests, Sister Elizabeth," replied Nancy with a smile.

Just like most households, the kitchen was a small building close to the main house; there were only a few steps to walk. Carrying the plentiful trays from the kitchen to the house, Nancy and Elizabeth were welcomed by helpful hands eager to help.

Other women walked over to the kitchen to fetch the additional trays, and soon children and adults were munching on gingersnaps and washing them down with cider. It was a noisy crowd, as they visited together.

The tall and lanky Reverend Richardson stood in the place of honor in his study and opened *The Vicar of Wakefield*. His brown eyes peered out of a pale face at the guests in his home; he was ready to take center stage once again, just as he did on Sundays in the pulpit.

Clearing his throat to get the crowd's attention, the thirty-two-year-old regally nodded to several of the men. This graduate of the University of Glasgow was an honorable man. He firmly believed in the value of education, and this was an opportunity to share it with his parishioners.

Not too long ago, Reverend Richardson had read a quote from the esteemed writer Benjamin Franklin. Franklin wrote, "Either write something worth reading

31

or do something worth writing about."

As he earnestly worked on writing his sermons each week, Richardson carefully chose the best words to encourage his flock. Richardson took all his responsibilities to heart and was demanding on himself. He preached often about God's grace, but the minister found it difficult to accept that grace for his own failings.

"Friends, I am pleased to begin the reading of my latest acquisition. Oliver Goldsmith is the author and has newly written a story of an English vicar by the name of Dr. Primrose. I finished the reading of this laudable book last night and was most encouraged by this cleric's sense of duty to his family. Forsooth, we will all be taught by this esteemed character."

Looking intently at some of the young boys in the audience, he remarked, "Scholars, I expect your attention to the reading tonight. You may expect questions next time we meet at the academy on what we cover tonight."

A few boys that attended the academy where Reverend Richardson was the teacher tried to sit up straighter, but others rolled their eyes or punched their neighbors. However, all gave a small sigh of relief that the text was in English and not Latin. Reading the classics was not their favorite subject during the school day.

The guests settled quietly on the few benches and chairs, floors, and steps, and the Reverend, after clearing his throat, commenced to read.

"However, when any one of our relations was found to be a person of very bad character, a troublesome guest, or one we desired to get rid of, upon his leaving my house for the first time, I ever took care to lend him a riding coat, or a pair of boots, or sometimes a horse of small value, and I always had the satisfaction of finding he never came back to return them.   "

Elizabeth closely watched her three sons; she was prepared to encourage their attention spans by sitting in their midst if they wavered in their listening. She knew that eight, six, and four-year-old boys contained more wiggles than they knew what to do with.

Hugh turned around to see where she was in the crowd, and his smile touched her heartstrings. With a little help from his Uncle James, the youngster had shot his first rabbit earlier in the day. Elizabeth had fried it for lunch, and Hugh was proud of his first hunting expedition.

The three boys were barefoot, and all three were going to need new breeches before cold weather. Elizabeth was amazed at their growing spurts over the summer. Usually, hand-me-downs worked from Hugh to Robert to Andy, but there were too many patches in all the pants this time. Elizabeth had cut and sewn their shirts much larger this year, so they would remain suitable and last longer.

Robert was the more reserved of the three, but he was the most competitive. Even though he was younger than Hugh, he wanted to keep up with his brother. Robert enjoyed playing horseshoes, and he would even play the game by himself. He had a good eye, and this would help him in his work of a farmer when he was an adult.

This social occasion was important in the building of their characters, and she continued to hope and pray that one of her three would be called to the ministry. Because he was an early reader, Elizabeth thought Andy showed the most promise. Studying for the ministry required much reading and scholarship. He was short-tempered and tended to argue to get his own way. Elizabeth had always heard that those with red hair tended to be besot with fiery tempers and sharp tongues. Andy's bright, red hair would never be an excuse for temper tantrums in her house! As she observed Andy rocking back-and-forth to stay awake, she realized he was a work in progress, as were her other two boys.

Elizabeth resolved to watch and pray over her sons. It was hard to be a single parent.

A Community's Loss
July 20, 1771

A few days later, one of Reverend Richardson's slaves ran up the road to the Crawford house shouting, "Miz. Jackson! Miz Jackson! Miz. Richardson sent me to fetch you. She needs help now!"

Elizabeth walked briskly out of the kitchen behind the house, untying her apron as she listened to the call. Waving to show she heard the message, Elizabeth turned back to pick up the extra loaf of bread she had baked that morning. Daily she baked at least one extra loaf, because there was always someone in need.

She tied her kerchief in a sling around her neck to hold the bread. Then Elizabeth slipped on her moccasins. Snatching her straw hat from the wooden peg on the wall, she tied the hanging ribbons into a bow under her chin.

Dashing to the field for her horse, she hollered to Jane on the porch, "Something's amiss at Nancy's! I will send word when I can."

The brown and white, short-legged marsh tacky grazed in the summer clover. Elizabeth's distinctive whistle and the call of his name perked up the horse's ears, and he looked in her direction. With a turn, Fire Foot trotted toward the fence.

By the time Elizabeth had reached the gate to open it, the horse met her. A halter and bit were hanging on the fence post for emergencies, and Elizabeth quickly adjusted them both to the horse's head. She scrambled up to the second rail of the fence and then climbed on the back of her mount.

With a few pats and words of encouragement, Elizabeth adjusted the reins. Fire Foot whinnied, shook his head and mane, and galloped up the road toward the

Williams' manse. The sure-footed horse sensed her urgency.

It was good to see the stubble in the shorn fields, as she rode by. Elizabeth was thankful for the fine wheat harvest earlier in the month. Three weeks ago, harvest time had arrived in the Waxhaws. The wheat plants were golden yellow, and the heads were limp and floppy. As a test, James had bitten the hard grain, and it crunched between his teeth. That was all the proof James needed. The harvest had been bounteous, and the bags filled with milled wheat in the barn were the confirmation.

As she concentrated again on her destination, Elizabeth prayed for her friend.

Whatever had happened must be a calamity; Nancy had never sent for her before. Fear clutched at her. She fought down the dread she felt.

The time riding to the Richardson home wasn't long, but the next few days and weeks were arduous and trying. Jumping off Fire Foot and throwing the reins to the ground, Elizabeth ran up the steps and opened the door.
Peering down the hall, only emptiness and shadows greeted Elizabeth.

"Nancy! Where are you? Nancy?" she shouted into the depths of the home.

Nancy appeared at the door of William's study. Her face was ashen, and her wide eyes were unfocused. She tightly held the doorframe for support before stumbling toward Elizabeth. Reaching her friend, Nancy grasped desperately for another crutch to keep herself standing. The minister's wife was crying hysterically, and tears rained down her face.

A somber William Byrd followed Nancy out of the study. He shook his head in disbelief. His unexpected visit to Reverend Richardson had not turned out as planned. Byrd had stopped to gain guidance from

Richardson for a new settlement of Irish settlers. He halted and remained in the doorway.

Looking over the shaking shoulders of her friend to the bewildered man, Elizabeth questioned him with her eyes. Nancy's whole body was now wracked with sobs of deep grief that filled the hall.

Finally, the sobs finally became whimpers. Elizabeth introduced herself.

"Goodday, sir, I am Elizabeth Jackson, a close friend and neighbor of Nancy's. Pray tell me what has happened?"

"I am grieved to say that we found Reverend Richardson dead in his study," William Byrd said softly.

Elizabeth shook her head in astonishment and horror. She had no words to respond to this stranger and no immediate assurances to comfort her friend.

She led Nancy to a rocking chair in the keeping room and guided her friend's limp body to the seat. She covered the minister's wife with a knitted shawl that had been placed on the back of the chair; Elizabeth remembered knitting it the past winter for her friend. The indigo color was their favorite. The shawl didn't stop Nancy's body from shaking or her low moans.

Elizabeth purposely walked back into the hall and toward the study. She wanted to shut the door of the study. William Byrd stepped out of her path but held out his arm to deter her. Though she appreciated his protective arm, Elizabeth shook her head and crossed the threshold.

She gasped in horror at the scene and froze in her tracks.

A piece of rope hung from the top beam of the room. There were frayed ends of different lengths that looked like hair that had not been combed.

Lying upside down, close to each other, were a tall stool and chair.

On the floor, with a bridle around his neck, lay the minister.

William Byrd had taken him down.

With a hand over her mouth, Elizabeth quietly closed the door. She had seen an unbelievable sight that was now seared in her mind. Now she understood Nancy's hysterics and panic. Elizabeth went straightaway to her friend's side.

Nancy's twelve-year marriage was over.

The date was July 20, 1771, a date that the Waxhaws community would never forget.

The elders of the church sent word to all the families about the death of their minister; no mention was made of the bridle around his neck. The leaders believed that it was singularly important to not betray Reverend Richardson's apparent suicide. His reputation, as well as the congregation's, would be tarnished.

All rallied around Nancy and attended her husband's funeral service the next day.

It wasn't long before word leaked out about the suicide, and a time of whispers and quiet accusations became a part of all adult conversations. His congregation remembered the debilitating headaches that plagued their minister. They talked about the solitary horse rides that had become more frequent for him that summer. Rather than his regular visits to their homes, he often rode past their farms without stopping. The adults wondered if there was anything they might have done to help their minister.

On Sundays, when Nancy entered the small meeting house, people nudged each other as she walked to her usual place on the front row. She heard comments like "remarkable piety," "only forty-two years old," "devoted to God." Nancy knew the words were not for her.

The community had doubts about Reverend

Richardson's suicide; the halter around his neck was a mystery. No one could understand how he could do that to himself, and they questioned Nancy's innocence in the matter.

Elizabeth started to spend more time at the manse because Nancy was lonely. Visitors became infrequent. To protect her friend from accusations, Elizabeth and her sons even sat with Nancy during the church services.

Relationships, once cordial and warm, were now strained. Quizzical looks and questioning eyes were difficult to handle when open hearts and arms had been the ordinary greetings before.

With no children to keep her occupied, Nancy's days were long.

She ordered an impressive grave marker for William's grave from Charlestown and was grateful when it was in place. She had carefully chosen the inscription and given details on the marble stone. Under the rounded top was a coat of arms with the words, "volumus et valemus." Then the words: "Here lies the body of the much-lamented Revd. William Richardson, M.A., Pastor of Waxhaw Congregation for 12 years and rested from his labours on the 20th Day of July, A.D. 1771. Aged 42 years."

His name was then engraved above a bust in low relief. Nancy was pleased with the chiseler's work; the carving was raised perfectly in the stone. At the bottom of the front were the words Nancy struggled to compose. "He lived to purpose. He preach'd with Fidelity. And being dead he speaks."

Elizabeth visited her friend every day; sometimes they only sat together and caught up on handwork. Nancy had little to mend, so she purposely worked on Elizabeth's bottomless basket of clothes and linens. Hugh, Robert, and Andy entertained the women with their wrestling in the yard. All diversions from Elizabeth and her sons prevented Nancy for a while from remembering her loneliness.

When the headstone arrived, the Presbyterian elders offered to help set it in place in the church cemetery. Obligation to their elected positions, as well as allegiance to their former minister, encouraged them to make this decision.

Elizabeth stood by her friend once again, as the elders strained to slide the stone off the wagon and put it in place. Nancy's grief was more tempered, but she could not keep the tears away.

"I want his congregation to remember him for the generous, godly man he was," Nancy softly said. "I wrote Charlestown with an addition to his headstone."

The stone was now upright, and the dirt mixed with rocks had steadied it in the ground. The two women walked around to the backside. Elizabeth clearly read aloud the words. "He left to the amount of 350 pounds sterling to purchase religious books for The Poor."

Memories grabbed their minds and then their hearts. The two widows stood isolated and deserted from the men who had walked back to the wagon and their horses. Providence had left Elizabeth and Nancy alone, but not friendless.

Providence changed again Nancy's life for the better when George Dunlap, a member of a large and wealthy local family, courted and married Nancy Richardson the following year.

Enthusiastically, Elizabeth celebrated her friend's new life, particularly Nancy's five children that she was eventually blessed with raising.

Sounds of War and Peace
November, 1774

Old King Cole was a merry old soul,
And a merry old soul was he;
He called for his pipe,
And he called for his bowl,
And he called for his fiddlers three.
Ev'ry fiddler had a fiddle,
And a very fine fiddle had he.

Tweedle dee, tweedle dee,
Tweedle dee, tweedle dee,
Tweedle dee, tweedle dee,
Went the fiddlers three,
Oh there's none so rare
As can compare,
With King Cole and his fiddlers three.

Spinning was a mindless task, so Elizabeth often sang while she worked. There was rhythm to *Old King Cole*, and her spinning wheel was keeping time with the lyrics. After a few repetitive verses, she would choose another song.

Elizabeth easily pulled the fibers apart, as one of her hands pinched the wool, and the other pulled the wool. Her feet had their own rhythm on the treadle to whatever song she was singing. Today's song was "Yankee Doodle" as she thought about recent events.

This morning she had put a little candle wax on the treadle because it was squeaking. The pulled fibers naturally wrapped around each other in repetition before they reached the spindle. Elizabeth was proud to be the spinner and weaver of cloth for the family. It was another act of patriotism, just like giving up the drinking of tea. Maybe one day, she mused, everyone would be proud of anything made in the colonies.

Already neighbors would buy or trade for any extra spun fiber or woven cloth from her spinning wheel and loom. Her hand spun wool and flax was durable, as well as soft. Elizabeth combined longer and coarser wool from some sheep with shorter and softer wool from others. Her painstaking choices of fibers made sure the clothes endured, even though they became stained and tattered. In fact, much was cut and stitched into something else.

It was a cold and overcast November day, but the warm glow from the fireplace and Elizabeth's humming and singing kept the outside gloom at bay.

James coughed again; his tread had been slow when he came in from the barn and fields. Bundled up by the fire, Jane stopped rocking and stared at her husband. Concern was on her face and in her eyes, but she chose to say nothing. Jane knew that after sipping a cup of hot apple cider, he would leave once again to complete his chores. He never left a job unfinished, and he taught this by example to all the children in their home.

When laziness attacked their work, James would loudly remind them, "God desires us to work. If a man doesn't work, he won't eat. Forsooth, the Good Book tells us this."

The boys would be home from school soon, and they would help. In the meantime, Jane had an idea for keeping James in the house a bit longer. She put down her knitting.

"Elizabeth, we haven't read the latest edition of the *South Carolina Gazette*. It would be so helpful to hear the goings-on in Charlestown and the low country. Perchance, could you rest your arms and feet to read us some from the paper?"

Putting the unspun wool back in the basket beside the spinning wheel, Elizabeth walked over to the cupboard and brought out the Charlestown paper. It was dated 21 November 1774. Elizabeth pulled her stool closer to the fireplace to be able to see better and began reading aloud from the first page.

CHARLESTOWN, November 7
On Tuesday last, Mr. Thomas Broughton jun. was married, to Miss Betsy Lesesne, a very amiable and accomplished young Lady, Daughter of the late Mr. Isaac Lesesne. The same Day arrived here, in the Ship Britannia, Capt. Samuel Ball, jun.
from London (amongst a Number of other Passengers....

Before Captain Ball had been many Hours in Port, the Committee of Observation were informed, that he had Seven Chests of Tea on board, subject to that Duty which all America have denied to be constitutionally imposed; and the Minds of the People appeared to be very much agitated. To allay the Ferment which there seemed reason to apprehend, that Committee met early on Wednesday Morning, sent for Captain Ball, who readily attended, and, after expressing to him their Concerns and Astonishment at his Conduct, acquainted him, it was expected the said Teas should not be landed here....

On Thursday at Noon, an Oblation was made to Neptune, of the said seven chests of Tea, by Messrs. Lindsay, Kinsley and Mackenzie them- selves; who going on board the Ship in the Stream, with their own Hands respectively stove the Chests belong to each, and emptied their Contents into the River, in the Presence of the Committee of Observation, who likewise went on board, and in View of the whole General Committee on the Shore besides numerous Concourse of People, who gave three hearty Cheers after the emptying of each Chest, and immediately after separated as if nothing had happened.

Between coughs, the smile on James' face grew wider as he listened. When Elizabeth finished reading, the soft-spoken, balding man stood abruptly, overturning his chair.

"Huzzah! I can see those merchants' long faces now, as they pitched their tea into the river. Seven chests full of tea bricks weighing over seven hundred pounds went swimming!" James cried out. "We came here for our freedom from the British. British taxes rob us of that right. We must stand firm against them."

James commenced to cough again and almost choked. He waved away the cup that Elizabeth offered him of the leftover cider, pulled his jacket and scarf back on, and marched to the door. Anxiously, Jane's eyes followed him. She knew better than to remonstrate with him about going back outside. James turned back to the sisters; they saw the glint of resolve in his eyes. "Mark my words, ladies. We will have our own time to stand tall against the British here in the Waxhaws. They are strong, but we are stronger. I won't let them take my land away from me," declared James.

His quiet closing of the door belied the force of his words.

As James walked away, they heard his voice raised in a popular Sons of Liberty song.

"Hearts of oak, are we still, for we're sons of those men,
"Hearts of oak, are we still, for we're sons of those men,
Who are always ready, steady, boys, steady, To fight for their freedom again and again!"

Elizabeth moved back to the spinning wheel, taking up where she had left off.

Jane, with clinched hands in her lap, kept thoughts of war invading her home at bay by purposely focusing on God's providence. They had already endured much in this new world, and she firmly believed God would give them the strength to endure even the British army at their front door.

With a dry mouth and a pounding heart, Jane softly spoke "Sister, do you remember when we received the news about the Boston Tea Party in the spring? The Sons of Liberty, dressed as Mohawk Indians, threw tea into the sea then."

Elizabeth smiled in recollection of the much talked-about event. "King George III closed the port of Boston in retaliation and demanded the money back for the tea. The man has no sense of humor."

She paused, and the sparkle went out of her eyes.

"Perchance, there might be a closing of Charlestown's harbor, too. It appears the British government is only satisfied when they receive more duties from us. We might need to depend solely on my spinning and weaving of cloth and not what comes on the ships.

Heretofore, Joseph Kershaw has kept us well supplied at his store in Pine Tree Hill. When James went on that last cattle drive to Charlestown, he told us about the flag on a pole near the Exchange building for all to see. It was blue, and the word liberty was sown in the middle."

Jane, with a vigorous nod, interrupted, "Aye, we from Ireland want nothing to do with British rule. Methinks, our southern neighbors are like-minded. Each time James visits Charlestown, he is stirred by the speeches he hears from the Sons of Liberty outside of town. Those secret meetings of the merchants under that oak tree in the pasture must be dangerous for all who attend. I admire their courage mightily, don't you, Elizabeth?"

Somberly, Elizabeth replied, "By the by, we, too, might be called to show that same courage. I pray I will be strong and not waver in doing the right thing."

Elizabeth stopped her spinning, stood up, and walked near the candlestick on the table. Finding the verse she sought, she read aloud from Deuteronomy 31:6. "Be strong and of a good courage, fear not, do not be afraid of them: for the LORD thy God, He it is that go with thee; He will not fail thee, nor for- sake thee."

There were tears in her eyes when she turned back to her sister. "Those were the words that Andrew read on our first night here to the colonies. He was a firm believer in reliance on God's providence, and I warrant he was aright."

At length, quiet reigned. The sisters pondered their present and their future.

*****

Several hours passed, and it was almost time for the day to end for the children. Elizabeth had been musing about the adult conversations of the afternoon. She believed their lives in the Waxhaws were about to change, along with all of the colonies. Even young Andy, at age seven, needed to be prepared.

Elizabeth put down her mending and abruptly spoke. " 'Tis a story that needs telling this night to those who will listen."

Ears perked up, and young eyes glanced in her direction.

She nodded to her own three and gestured them to quiet themselves. Soon the floor was crowded with upturned faces lifted in her directions. Some were on their bottoms; others sprawled lengthwise in any available space. They were leaning on each other, along with a few arms and legs pushing for more room. Minutes passed until comfort was eventually found by all, and Elizabeth started her story.

"It was over five hundred years ago in the Old Country of Scotland, and William Wallace was born. He had two brothers, one older and one younger, like you Robert."

She paused to pat her middle son's arm.

"William grew up to be a tall man, over six feet. He was exceeding strong and easily used a claymore sword. His sword was over three feet long. Its blade was steel."

Elizabeth stood and pulled Andy up from the floor and turned him to face the others. She held her hand over Andy's head and commenced to talk again.

"That sword would have been longer than Andy is tall. The long reach of the blade would have kept enemies from getting too close. Forsooth, they might have turned away rather than face that patriot."

As both Andy and Elizabeth sat back down, Hugh asked, "What is a patriot, Mama?"

Elizabeth didn't hesitate in answering her oldest son.

"A patriot is someone who loves their country and is willing to fight for it. A patriot is always loyal to his country, and he works hard to make it better."

Leaning forward in his chair, James interrupted with a question, "How many patriots in this house?"

A barrage of loud, affirmative answers from all in the room made him smile, as he sat back.

"Zounds, we must be a household of patriots," he remarked. " 'Tis a good thing, it is."

He turned to Elizabeth, "It is my opinion that

more is to be learned from William Wallace."

Her storytelling continued.

"William Wallace loved Scotland, but he disliked En- gland. Invited by the Scottish lords to make peace among them, the English King Edward I took over the country. William rebelled against the English rule and became a hunted outlaw, but he led only thirty men in fighting for their independence in small battles. Soon more men joined the patriots.

"One day near the Forth River, the English army gathered its forces of 50,000 soldiers to fight William Wallace and his 5,000 men. The Scottish army watched their enemy march over the hill moving closer and closer to the bridge. They knew they were in trouble.

"Wallace smiled to himself. He knew the bridge was narrow, and only a few men could cross at one time. When the English soldiers tried to cross, the Scottish soldiers started their attack. The bridge collapsed, and more English soldiers drowned. Part of the English army tried to cross upriver, but the Scots won this battle, too. William Wallace and his soldiers took the field and celebrated their victory. They were all heroes.

It is called the Battle of Stirling Bridge, because it was close to Stirling Castle. Until the end of his life, when he was captured by the English, William Wallace never stopped fighting for Scotland's freedom. Everyone remembers him, even today, for his strength and courage."

For a few moments, there was silence in the room. Then there was an eruption of "Huzzahs!"

The single mother looked at her three sons to see what their reaction was to this hero.

Hugh's eyes glistened, as he pictured himself carrying a claymore sword like William Wallace. His young body did not have the strength, but his heart and mind caught the vision. Robert straightened his shoulders when he stood up. There was a seriousness to the boy's face that was beyond his years. It was clear he now understood what a patriot was and knew that was a path he wanted to follow. Even young Andy, with all his shenanigans, turned his head to the side and looked beyond her to something only he could see.

The impact of the story had not fallen on deaf ears that night. Hugh interrupted his mother's watching with the words.

"I believe I know another patriot that lives in the colonies, Mama, and we have one of his books. Hugh walked over to the sparse bookshelf and brought back their copy of *Poor Richard's Almanac*.

"Benjamin Franklin writes a lot. But I remember our schoolmaster making us copy on our slates one day another of his sayings, and it has stuck with me.

Franklin said, 'Those who would give up essential liberty to purchase a little temporary safety, deserve neither liberty nor safety.' Appears to me this man is a patriot like William Wallace and our family."

The Battle of Sullivan's Island
July, 1775

As Elizabeth watched the war games being played in the front yard, she mused that there were no fence sitters on this farm. The faces of her three sons fighting imaginary Tories were stern and unsmiling. Her boys had moved from their games of being soldiers following William Wallace in Scotland to those following General George Washington. The English continued to be the enemy, both in the past and the present.

Two years had passed since the Charlestown Tea Party. In 1775, British troops had fired on minutemen in Lexington. George Washington was now commander-in-chief of the Continental Army; he was appointed by the Second Continental Congress. The fort in Charlestown had been attacked but repulsed the British. Almost weekly, riders stopped at the Crawford farm with news of the rebellion.

Elizabeth's three sons now listened with eager ears for all war news. They even asked questions of their Uncle James on a daily basis. The common conversation uniting young and old was war.

Hugh, Robert, and Andy were all similar in build; they took after their father. No matter how much they ate, the fourteen, twelve, and ten-year-olds were skinny with long legs. Hugh and Robert had Andrew's brown eyes, but Andy had inherited her blue ones. They varied little in height or with their angular faces. Being small of stature, Elizabeth had to now look up to her two oldest and knew it would be the same with Andy soon.

Even so, Elizabeth demanded her sons' respect. Her parents had taught her the importance of obeying the Ten Commandments, and she believed the Good Book.

There was a promise in the fifth commandment that said, "Honor thy father and thy mother; that thy days may be long upon the land which the Lord thy God giveth thee." They mostly listened to her, but sometimes she had to remind them of the consequences of showing disrespect. No one could mistake the brothers' kinship or their allegiance to each other. They stood together when one of them was singled out by others but gave no quarter to each other in their wrestling.

"Aye, I have you now!" hollered Andy with a whoop.

With a hard push of both his arms and legs, Andy came off the ground once again and grabbed Robert around his waist. The momentum landed them both in the grass, and they rolled as one across the yard. Each tried to dominate the other with a grip that would not be loosened. Hugh became the referee and the coach to each brother.

"Don't let him pin you, Robert. Take heed of his elbows he is want to use. Andy is younger than you, but he is a strong one. Ah, Andy, your motto is to not stay throwed. Robert almost has you locked down. Ye best get up now; your time is almost over."

With a smile on his face, Hugh took no sides in this fight. With enthusiasm, he thumped his fist on the ground moving from one side of the fracas to the other.

As they rolled in the red dirt, Elizabeth watched the earth and sweat become part of the clothes she had washed only yesterday. These late days of summer in late July and now August had been dry, and the dust migrated and stuck to both man and beast.

Elizabeth turned back to her work on the loom, and the clack, thump sound turned into background noise for the scuffling boys. Because of the early spring, she had planted the flax seeds at the first of April. The weather was cooperative with the exact amounts of needed rain and sun, and by late May those beautiful blue flowers abundantly adorned the field.

One day a flock of ducks landed in the middle of the field. It was an astounding sight. The fowl obviously mistook the lavish growth of flowers for water, but they soon flew to a more welcoming river.

Elizabeth made a face, thinking back to those days of dyeing the flax in the large, iron pots over the hot fire. It was a sweltering week for such heated work, and some threads were not the true color in Elizabeth's imagination. She had never been satisfied with second best, so the process had to be repeated.

Elizabeth was now delighted with the colors of the skeins next to the loom. The reds and oranges from the madder root were vibrant. The hue from the indigo was akin to the Carolina night sky, and the skeins dyed with the goldenrod were as cheerful and intense as the sunrays beaming on the porch as she worked.

"I'll never give up," shouted Andy.

Elizabeth looked over at the boys again. All three were lying on their backs; their chests were heaving with the exertions of their wrestling. There were gasps for more air from all three. But the grins on their faces spoke for the words they could not utter. Nods of a time well spent also silently acknowledged the occasion. Elizabeth's reaction, with a puzzled tilt to her face, was to negatively shake her head. She honestly did not understand this need of men and boys to prove they were the best, even in fun.

Hugh suddenly jumped up. "First one to the well," he bellowed, as he took off to the side of the house.

His lanky frame charged for the cold water that his body demanded. The other two were close behind, but Hugh's head start gave him the edge. He was slurping water from the gourd hanging on the bucket before his brothers arrived.

More horseplay fired up as a water fight erupted. For the brothers, each day was a contest that involved their siblings. All wanted the crown of victory, and Elizabeth was glad the crown moved from one son to another. Hard feelings were short-lived since the victors frequently swapped places. Because of their demanding and full days, there was little time for sour grapes.

The drenched and laughing boys marched around the house, walked up the two steps to the porch, and fell into various positions around their mother.

Hugh was the first to settle down. "Momma, I've been thinking about this war with the British. King George gave us this land to live on. We brothers even own the land that Papa and you lived on. You showed us the title to our 200 acres. If we have proof that it is ours, why are we fighting for it now?"

Elizabeth thought before she spoke; she needed an example that her sons could relate to. "Hugh, it doesn't really make sense that we should have to fight for our land if we own it. The taxes that King George III and Parliament have imposed on us are unfair.

Those in the Continental Congress have written to the King over and over asking him to rethink his policies, but Parliament continues to demand more money from us. We have no one to represent us in Parliament. The British government tends to take what they want when they want it.

This is why your papa, and I came to this colony to begin with. The taxes were too high in Scotland, and there was no way for us to make ends meet. It was hard to leave and start over in a new country, but we made this decision for our future and you boys. Your papa worked hard those two years before he died."

Elizabeth paused a minute and then smiled.

"Andrew would often say, 'Hard work never

hurt anybody.' It is important for us to work hard to keep what he gave us and let no one take it away. If we must fight for our freedom, we will fight."

Robert swiftly agreed. "I see, Mamma. It's a personal fight for us. We must defend what is ours, even if it means war. Aye, it is akin to our wrestling while ago. It was a struggle, but we didn't stop until one of us won. We colonists won't quit fighting until we win!"

"I want to fight those soldiers that want to rob us. I have my own rifle and am ready to practice with our militia next Training Day,"

Andy jumped to his feet with these words. "Why do I have to be twelve before I can train to be a soldier?"

Hugh answered his brother before Elizabeth could.

"Andy, I figure there will be plenty of time for you to practice with us before we send those British soldiers back across the sea. I will begin today teaching you what I have learned from the older men. Then you will be sure and ready when your time comes."

Andy nodded his assent of being able to start his soldier training that very day and sat back down.

Robert continued the conversation.

"King George blockaded the Boston harbor two years ago, and that put many men out of work. I remember when we heard the townspeople were starving. Our community started sending supplies to them. We all worked together to help our neighbors survive. It appears to me that fighting together will work well, too."

Hugh had picked up his knife and was whittling a soldier out of a scrap of wood lying on the porch. As he stared at his brother and spoke, he stopped, gripping the knife in one hand.

"Don't forget that Uncle James and his men were at the battle in Charlestown in June. He went from home to home asking our neighbors to join him in fighting the British. I can see them now as they rode down the lane with Uncle James leading them. They were all volunteers, but they were ready to help fight for their freedom."

He looked reproachfully at his mother, as he recalled Elizabeth's emphatic "nay" to his most reasonable request in his thinking, to travel with Uncle Robert.

"I still think I should have gone with our neighbors and uncle."

Elizabeth decided to only listen for the time being to what her sons were saying. She needed to know what they were thinking. She encouraged them to continue by stopping her work on the loom. Its noise might interrupt their thoughts.

"There were nine war ships that fought Colonel William Moultrie and his men, but our soldiers didn't give up. They battled for ten hours to win! They must have been tough soldiers to fight that long," said Andy.

Elizabeth looked up to see her brother-in-law, James, walking up the path with his rifle over his shoulder. He was carrying a large turkey under his other arm. Elizabeth waved at him to join the porch gathering. The Jackson boys heartily greeted their uncle. They were hoping for a retelling of the battle in Charlestown.

"Uncle James, tell us again about the battle at Fort Sullivan again. Mayhap, you might remember a new portion," said Hugh eagerly. Hugh stood up and moved beside his brothers to give his uncle more space.

Elizabeth picked up her knitting. It was a quiet task that would not intrude in the conversation.

Robert sat down and leaned back on the outside walls of his house. He pulled the clay pipe out of his haversack and packed it down before he lit it. All who knew Robert understood this was his first task as soon as he sat down. Finally, he nodded to his oldest nephew.

"We crossed from Charlestown to Sullivan's Island on a ferry. The horses were skittish, but all the men remembered what it was like to be on a small boat in an ocean. The salt spray irritated our eyes, but the distance was short to the wharf.

"I remember seeing the blue flag flying over the fort in the distance. The vivid blue of the background could be seen from afar. As we rode closer, we saw the crescent in the left corner. I heard tell later that Colonel Moultrie called it the "Liberty Flag." It is a flag to be proud of because Carolina defeated the British navy that day.

The men were still building the walls of the fort when we arrived. It was a strange sight to see palmetto logs filled in with sand from the island. There was no stone available on the island, so Colonel Moultrie used those palmetto trees. His men from the Second South Carolina Regiment worked steadily for months, but only two sides were completed when we arrived. The most important wall, the one that held the heavy guns, was completed. Its structure was of brick and wood, and thirty-one cannons were lined beside each other across the rampart.

"Those cannons were a fearsome sight.

"We joined with the building of more sixteen-foot-thick walls. It took many trees and wagons full of sand to make those walls thick. The sand blew in our faces, and the heat from the sun appeared to bounce off the sand into our eyes. Mosquitoes flew around us constantly, but we slapped at them and kept working. By each night, my arms were covered with their infernal bites At least, I had the satisfaction of sending many of them to kingdom come each day."

James Crawford grinned at the picture in his mind.

"Swatting mosquitoes became a sport for us. We challenged each other to contests to see who could whack the most at one time. Watching grown men, not children mind ye, waiting to see how many mosquitoes would land on their arms or legs before they killed them was quite comical.

Absentmindedly, James scratched at his arm, as if those low country mosquitoes had followed him home.

"The bread and fresh shrimp we ate every night helped us to forget the daily challenges. That was the tastiest seafood I have ever enjoyed. We felled, cut, and carried trees to the fort site. From where we worked, we could see the British ships in the harbor. One of the men told me they had been in the harbor getting ready to attack for almost three weeks.

"Each day we also conducted military drills. Keeping the rifles cleaned and the cannons prepared was necessary preparation, just like building the fort. Two soldiers I met were Francis Marion and Thomas Sumter. We had some mighty fine talks about what our lives would be like here without the British and their infernal taxes. I would be proud to fight with them again.

"On June 28, the battle commenced. I watched a fleet of the King's warships sail into the harbor with their sails open. Our drummer beat To Arms. We took our places behind the walls."

The boys' eyes were glued on their uncle, as he relived that first day of battle in his life.

"As they moved closer to the island, it was a chilling sight. As far as I could see, there were ships with cannons pointed straight at me. Before long, I could see the sailors standing at their posts on the ships. The commanders were dressed in decorated uniforms. I saw Commodore Sir Peter Parker raise his battle sword over his head, and with a slash lowered his sword. Immediately, a signal flag was raised, and the bombardment began.

Appeared to me, it was significant to mark the time. I glanced at my pocket watch; it was nigh 11:00 a.m. A man's first battle is of weighty consequence."

James stopped to puff on his pipe.

Leaning forward, Andy asked, "How loud were the cannons and rifle fire, Uncle James?"

"Aye, my lad, my ears rang for days after the battle. Imagine thunderclaps booming all at the same time, both around ye and beside ye. Remember, too, it was cannons on two sides of the water. Truly, I am surprised I am not stone deaf to this day.

"The British had many more guns that we did, and they fired endlessly. Their cannon balls would strike the fort, and sometimes the fort would shake. But it didn't catch fire because those hot balls buried themselves either in the sand or in those palmetto logs. Men on both sides were wounded and lost their lives, but the endless firing continued.

"All of a sudden, a British cannonball hit the flagstaff, and it broke it half. The flag and part of the pole fell outside the fort wall. In astonishment, I watched a soldier jump over the wall, retrieve the flag, and climb back into the safety of the fort between gunfire and cannon fire. Watching him, I found myself holding my breath. That soldier's chances were slim, but he safely ran back the same way. He did what needed doing mighty well. Huzzah! Huzzah! We shouted, as he climbed back over the wall."

James raised his arm in salute with these words before he continued.

"Grabbing another pole, men wrestled to reattach the flag. Urgency propelled their hands to send the flag flying above the fort in short order once again. Within minutes, our Liberty Flag flew proudly in the breeze."

"Uncle James, who was the soldier that saved the flag?" questioned Robert.

"His name was Sergeant William Jasper, Robert. I was proud to serve with him, as well as all my fellow soldiers, that day.

"They were all heroes. There were no cowards behind the walls of Fort Sullivan.

"During a battle, my boys, there are always many acts of bravery that save lives or turn the tide. There was no escape from the smoke of the rifles and cannon blasts burning our eyes. Men risked their lives to bring fresh water and food to us that were on the firing line. Others tended the wounded and dying. Our supply of gunpowder dwindled, and our cannons' fire slowed. But then we received more gunpowder from Charlestown. Brave men sailed across the channel to bring it to us."

"The battle lasted until around 9:00 that night until our ammunition was low again. As the tide went out, the enemy weighed their anchors and traveled away from the island with that tide.

"Several times we have read that pamphlet, *Common Sense*, written by Thomas Paine," remarked Elizabeth. "After listening to you, James, methinks his words in the introduction are worthy of remembrance. I memorized these during the winter to remind me of this stand we have taken against Britain.

"These are the times that try men's souls. The summer soldier and the sunshine patriot will, in the crisis, shrink from the service of their country; but he that stands it now, deserves the love and thanks of men and women.'"

"James, I salute you and the men who fought with you at Sullivan's Island. Nary one of you will ever shrink from fighting for our country, even if the cost is high. I will fight with you."

James Crawford

Young Andy Jackson

Hugh, Robert, and Andy

Robert and Andy

Marsh Tackies

Carolina Parakeets

Cabin in Winter

Elizabeth reading her Bible

The Declaration of Independence July, 1776

Elizabeth gathered together the skeins of spun flax and pieces of woven cloth in her bedroom. They were in all kinds of split oak baskets, even one egg basket, and in piles all over the floor. The colors tumbled together in disarray. She had plenty of orders to deliver to her friends and neighbors today, but the finished products needed to be separated first.

She sorely missed her sister Jane. It had been almost a year since Jane died, but still Elizabeth had to stop herself from calling out her name. The sisters had grown closer still in the years that Elizabeth was a welcome housekeeper and second mother to Jane's children.

From childhood, they had created play times out of their work. Often, they had sung songs or recited nursery rhymes to make the clock and tasks move faster. With smiles at those remembrances, Elizabeth piled the yarn in one basket and the cloth in another, swiftly bringing order out of jumble. As wee lassies, the two sisters had even learned to count from one of those rhymes.

Watching to be sure all would fit in each basket, Elizabeth recited, as she organized the baskets.

> *One, two buckle my shoe*
> *Three, four, knock at the door*
> *Five, six, pick up sticks*
> *Seven, eight, lay them straight*
> *Nine, ten, a big fat hen*
> *Eleven, twelve, dig and delve*
>
> *Thirteen, fourteen, maids a'courting Fifteen,*

sixteen, maids in the kitchen Seventeen,
eighteen, maids in waiting Nineteen, twenty, my
plate's empty.

Elizabeth could almost hear her mother's daily refrain to her daughters as they were growing up, "Satan will find mischief for idle hands."

A chuckle was Elizabeth's response to that memory, knowing that there was never any idle time for her. Hugh, Robert, and Andy all needed new shirts because they had grown so tall this summer. It took three yards to make a man's shirt, so Elizabeth knew there was much more work on the loom ahead of her.

Piling up some of the smaller baskets on top of the larger ones and straightening those askew, Elizabeth finally moved through the keeping room toward the porch. She was glad to be uncluttering her room; she preferred to have everything neatly in its place.

She placed the baskets to the right of the door near her loom. Thinking there might be time to work on the new coverlet she had started, Elizabeth picked up the wooden shuttle.

Hearing the first sounds of horses' hoofs and the rattle of wagon wheels, Elizabeth realized her neighbors were gathering. Her three sons were in the wheat field with their Uncle James. She saw them running toward the house from afar. It was time for the spring wheat to be harvested and then the winter wheat planted. Elizabeth hoped there was good news to be shared to the community this day.

As she watched her three sons race in from the wheat fields, she wondered what their futures held. Hugh and Robert both favored working the land. Mayhap they would one day farm their inheritance of land from their father on Twelve Mile Creek.

The proud mother was still astounded that Andy

had learned to read at age five and to write well at eight. His spelling was creative, though, with few words being spelled the same way twice. She didn't believe her dream of Andy becoming a minister of the gospel was to be a reality in his future. He saw no worth in the classics. Greek and Latin studies were a prerogative for careers in law, medicine, and the church.

Both of Andy's teachers, William Humphries and later James White Stephenson, saw his potential, but they also recognized his lack of interest in the scholar's world. At age ten, there was no inkling as to what her youngest might choose to make his living.

Realizing this wool-gathering was a waste of time, Elizabeth walked down the steps to meet their friends.

Elizabeth could see the beginning of a long line of wagons, filled with children and adults, rolling around the bend. The men and young boys rode on thoroughbreds and marsh tackies. Family dogs had shadowed their families, and there was delighted jumping, barking, and chasing as they greeted each other. Before long, the front of the Crawford house was strewn with playing children and huddled adults.

The word had spread quickly about the arrival of the new broadside, the single sheet printed on one side. Along with letters, yesterday's rider from Charlestown also carried a rolled newspaper copy. Peter Timothy, the editor of the *South Carolina Gazette,* had printed copies to be distributed.

The Waxhaws community anxiously craved the latest news from the Low Country. There were twelve families that occupied the fifteen-mile radius. The hub was the Waxhaws Meeting House. Most of the families were related. Elizabeth looked forward to seeing her other three sisters today.

James slowly meandered through the crowd,

greeting, and speaking to the large group assembled in front of his home. Wives made themselves comfortable sitting on the ground with their youngest children. Their husbands stood with arms crossing their chests waiting to hear the latest news. It must be significant because all of them had left their wheat fields.

There was camaraderie amongst the crowd and amidst the families. Through the years they had worshiped together and worked together. They had loaned farm tools to each other and celebrated births. Helping each other build houses and fences were memories that wove them together, just like their standing beside a grieving wife or husband. Their actions spoke louder than their words. The Scotch-Irish were clannish, and there was strength in their solidarity.

Walking up the steps to the porch, Robert motioned to Andy to follow him. Then James rang the large bell that hung from the porch. Before the harsh bell's clangs had faded, an expectant hush had descended on the crowd.

James picked up the broadside that was lying on a place of honor on a small table and handed it to Andy. Andy walked to the center of the top step and commenced to read, first the title and then the words of the printed document:

In Congress, July 4, 1776
The Unanimous Declaration of the thirteen United
States of America

WHEN in the Course of human Events, it becomes
necessary for one People to dissolve the Political Bands
which have connected them with another, and to assume
among the Powers of the Earth, the separate and equal
Station to which the Laws of Nature and of Nature's God
entitle them, a de- cent Respect to the Opinions of

Mankind requires, that they should declare the Causes which impel them to the Separation., We hold these Truths to be self-evident, that all men are created equal, that they are endowed by their Creator with certain unalienable Rights, that among these are Life, Liberty, and the Pursuit of Happiness - That to secure these Rights, Governments are instituted among Men, deriving their just Powers From the Consent of the Governed, that whenever any Form of Government becomes destructive of these Ends, it is the Right of the People to alter or to abolish it, and to institute new Government, laying its Foundation on such Principles, and organizing its, and distant from the Depository of their public Records, for the sole Purpose of fatiguing them into Compliance with his Measure...He has plundered our Seas, ravaged our Coasts, burnt our Towns, and destroyed the Lives of our People:, He is, at this Time, transporting large Armies of foreign Mercenaries to compleat the Works of Death, Desolation, and Tyranny, already begun with Circumstances of Cruelty and Perfidy, scarcely paralleled in the most barbarous Ages, and totally unworthy the Head of a civilized Nation..., In every Stage of these Oppressions we have petitioned for Redress in the most humble Terms: Our repeated Petitions have been answered only by repeated Injury. A Prince, whose Character is thus marked by every Act which may define a Tyrant, is unfit to be the Ruler of a free People:, Nor have we been wanting in Attentions to our British Brethren. We have warned them from Time to Time of Attempts by their Legislature to extend an unwarrantable Jurisdiction over us. We have reminded them of the Circumstances of our Emigration and Settlement here. We have ap- pealed to their native Justice and Magnanimity, and we have conjured them by the Ties of our common Kindred to disavow these Usurpations, which, would inevitably interrupt our

Connections and Correspondence. They too have been deaf to the Voice of Justice and of Consanguinity. We must, therefore, acquiesce in the Necessity, which denounces our Separation, and hold them, as we hold the rest of Mankind, Enemies in War, in Peace, Friends., We, therefore, the Representatives of the UNITED STATES OF AMERICA, in GENERAL CONGRESS, Assembled, appealing to the Supreme Judge of the World for the Rectitude of our Intentions, do, in the Name, and by Authority of the good People of these Colonies, solemnly Publish and Declare, that these United Colonies are, and of Right ought to be, FREE AND INDEPENDENT STATES; that they are absolved from all Allegiance to the British Crown, and that all political Connection between them and the State of Great Britain, is and ought to be totally dissolved; and that as FREE AND INDEPENDENT STATES, they have full Power to levy War, conclude Peace, contract Alliances, establish Commerce, and to do all other Acts and Things which INDEPENDENT STATES may of Right do. And for the Support of this Declaration, with a firm Reliance on the Protection of Divine Providence, we mutually pledge to each other our Lives, our Fortunes, and our sacred Honour.

Andy had practiced reading the declaration the night before several times to his family. Each repetition gave him familiarity with the words and phrases. Strong language was behind every thought chosen in the 1,337 word document.

A woodpecker hunting food in a nearby tree interrupted the sound of the boy's voice. Occasionally, one of the dogs barked, and a baby whimpered. There were echoes of the children playing down the road. The adults didn't want to be distracted, so the children were given freedom to entertain themselves.

73

But throughout the reading, the adults' attention was fixed on hearing and understanding this document called the Declaration of Independence.

Robert Crawford, James' brother, was the first to break the silence.

"Those are powerful words written by men who understand our grievances against Britain. Andy, can you read the signatures of the signers? We might recognize some names."

Andy complied, and there were nods to familiar names like John Adams, and Thomas Jefferson. Several more recognized the four signers from South Carolina: Edward Rutledge, Thomas Lynch, Jr., Arthur Middleton, and Thomas Heyward, Jr. The Waxhaws community acknowledged the names of their Low Country neighbors with huzzahs!

James took the broadside from Andy and spoke loudly to the crowd. He wanted everyone to hear him.

"I have had an opportunity to read these words several times, and this is your first hearing of them. But these heroic men are resolved to sacrifice their very lives to these United States of America. The Second Continental Congress has confronted the King of England.

"There are twenty-seven abuses that he is charged with."

With a louder voice, James exclaimed, "We don't belong to England anymore! We are free from their lawlessness and taxes! We have rights! We will stand tall together and push those British soldiers back across the Atlantic Ocean!"

After each phrase, the fervent voices of the men and women hollered a resounding "Aye!"

For almost an hour, there were various adult conversations on that tract of land in the Upcountry. No one truly understood what would happen next. But they all grasped and held fast to the thoughts of their individual freedom from Britain.

A Visit from Lafayette
June, 1777

With a basket over her arm, Elizabeth slowly wandered toward the peach orchard. For a change, she was taking her time enjoying the early summer day.

She was barefoot, and the red clay of the worn path was cool to her feet. A low branch snatched her cap, but her calloused hands rescued it and replaced it on her head. Her mother had always modeled neatness in her dress, no matter the task at hand. Though Elizabeth tried to follow that example of tidiness, it was a taxing struggle some days.

She swung the basket, as a child would, and skipped along the uneven path. Relishing the sights and sounds, the widow marveled at the green leaves, the gentle whisper of the wind, and the chatter of various birds. There was the familiar cooing sound of the turtledoves.

Particularly in the spring and summer, Elizabeth admired daily the garden that she now called home.

She was hankering for a peach pie, and the early fruit was ripe, even though it was small. Taking a moment for herself, she pondered the latest news of the war. A rider had brought a new broadside yesterday with the news of a flag adopted by the Second Continental Congress for their new country.

Elizabeth pictured the simple design in her mind. This official flag of the United States was to be thirteen stripes representing the thirteen states. The stripes would alternate in the colors of red and white. On a blue background would be a constellation of thirteen, five- pointed stars.

Elizabeth wanted to make a United States flag. Knowing she had plenty of her favorite indigo blue cloth woven, she wondered if her elderberry bushes were still producing the bright red fruit that would be needed.

She changed her course to the orchard and walked to the right toward the sunny portion of land so loved by the elderberry. The crop of berries was overwhelming this year, but the dried berries would be delicious in pies this winter. From the time she saw the abundance of those fragrant, small, white flowers, Elizabeth knew a lavish crop would be there for the picking. She had already made pies, jam, and wine from the dark, purple berries, but there should still be plenty to make red dye.

As she arrived within view of the elderberry bushes that were now as large as small trees, she saw several deer enjoying the bounty. As soon as they captured her scent or heard her footsteps, Elizabeth knew they would sprint speedily away. This fruit was the favorite of other wildlife, like turkeys, chipmunks, squirrels, and many birds as well. The profusion of these bushes provided enough for all.

All three of the deer raised their heads from their berry munching, turned swiftly, and ran off. In another direction hopped two rabbits. A bevy of small finches flew toward the sky. Elizabeth had interrupted the menagerie's meal, but she knew they would be back and probably bring their relatives. For now, the fruit was left solely to her.

Lifting some of the heavier branches, Elizabeth picked several and munched the tart berries. She knew the taste would be bitter without adding sugar, but she had always liked their biting flavor. Cooking enhanced their taste.

As she turned away from the large bushes and back to the path, she marveled at the ease with which plants usually grew in the Waxhaws. Aye, they needed to be tended, but she enjoyed the variety here in the

Carolinas. Thinking some more, Elizabeth knew there was nothing about her new country that she didn't approve of.

Heading back to the peach orchard, she heard the sounds of horses and carriages in the distance. The post road continued to bring travelers their way. Mayhap, they would have company again today. She would pick more peaches in the event that was so.

As Elizabeth drew closer to the peach trees, she glimpsed the familiar red heads of many Carolina parakeets. She was glad that neither James nor any of the boys were with her. They would have been tempted to use them as target practice. Without the boys, Elizabeth could enjoy the beauty of the flock.

The small birds were only a foot long, but fields of corn and fruit orchards were the chosen dining place for them. As adults, they weighed only a pound. Elizabeth had also heard tell of their feathers being popular in women's hats sold in the millinery shops in Charlestown. At some of the plantations in the Low Country, these exotic birds were actually kept as pets.

Stopping for a moment, Elizabeth was struck by the picture of the birds among the leaves of the trees. She listened to their chattering; these birds were voluble, but the sound was pleasant. Their green plumage, with the small patch of yellow on the tail, blended in with the foliage. Their bright yellow necks and blood-orange heads added unmistakable color with the trees. She wished she could weave a pattern of those colors for a coverlet and appreciated its beauty in her mind.

Realizing she was near to disrupting the tableau, Elizabeth walked forward. Before she reached the trees, all sizes of Carolina parakeets took flight. They appeared to move simultaneously.

Last year, James had shot an adult parakeet above his cornfields. The flock circled the dead bird on the ground and would not fly away. The alarm and distress calls were quite loud. The birds refused to leave the scene. James chose not to take advantage of their continued presence in the air that day.

As Elizabeth picked peaches to fill her basket, she hoped this small crowd of birds would go back to their roosting place and stay away from their peaches and corn this summer. With their sharp beaks, the seeds, nuts, or fruit were not safe.

Sounds from the front yard were louder now and drew Elizabeth away from the birds. Her time alone savoring nature and its bounty, a gift from the Creator, was ended for today. Switching roles in her mind to the one of her role as hostess conveying hospitality directed her feet back to minding her homestead.

There were more than a dozen men, their mounts, and a lone carriage close to the porch. Elizabeth didn't recognize their uniforms. Their short, blue coats were a different hue than the Continental soldiers. She recognized their speech as being French, which Elizabeth didn't speak.

One young man jumped from the carriage that wobbled because of a loose wheel. His boots easily planted themselves on the road in front of the house. There was a contrasting red collar and cuffs trimmed in gold braid on his coat. He deliberately brushed his white breeches and vest. The dust and dirt had disappeared in the black color of his boots and boot spats and was not as evident.

Then he saw Elizabeth. He smiled at her and made a formal bow in her direction. With his black, bicorn hat sweeping behind him in one hand, he bent low.

Elizabeth duly noted his aristocratic and military backgrounds, reflected in both his manners and uniform, as well as the way he resembled her own three sons.

Elizabeth nodded her acknowledgment in return, made a swift curtsy, and walked toward the young man.

A taller and older man made his way to the side of the youth and greeted Elizabeth in similar fashion.

"*Madame*," the broad-shouldered elder addressed Elizabeth in a pleasing accent of understandable English. "My name is Baron Johan De Kalb, and my young friend here is Marie Joseph Paul Yves Roche Gilbert du Molier, Marquis de Lafayette. Along with the soldiers accompanying us, we seek lodging for the night. Perchance, you have room?"

"Aye, we have floor space to accommodate you and your men in the keeping room or on the porch, or you can pitch tents close to the house, sir."

The young, nineteen-year-old bowed once again with the same graciousness. Even though his upper-class training was evident, there was no superiority in his manner. Lafayette gave the impression he was as comfortable in the Upcountry, as he was in the French court he had recently left.

Slower in his speech, and obviously not as fluent as De Kalb, Lafayette slowly said, "*Bonjour, Madame. Good day!* Ah, *magnifique! Je la'ime votre* pays."

The mix of French and English showed the newness of English for Lafayette, but his excitement in being in Carolina was obvious. His eyes darted from the landscape to the house to the fields in rapid succession, as if he were taking pictures for remembrance.

Elizabeth saw Andy in the distance working in the fields. She hollered and waved to him to join them. Quickly he was by her side in his bare feet, ragged breeches, and stained shirt; he nodded to the soldiers.

"Andy, go fetch Dr. Cantzon. Ask him to come to supper, please, and bring his family. Our guests are from France, and we want to make them comfortable here in the Waxhaws."

The ten-year-old boy took off to locate his Marsh Tacky named Washington. The two-year-old, tan horse with the black mane and Andy were good friends. They had herded cattle together a few days before, and Washington proved once again his sense of balance.

Thinking about all the extras for their evening meal, Elizabeth calculated about how large a ham should be brought in from the smokehouse. Thoughtfully, she figured six chickens would also be necessary. She hadn't planned on either guests or a happening when she wandered to the peach orchard, but, for sure, more peaches must be fetched to feed this crowd. She turned back to the gentlemen and the other soldiers.

"John Cantzon is our doctor, and we fare better with him in our community. His parents were French Huguenots, and John has taught his daughters his parents' language. I believe you will enjoy visiting with them tonight.

The well is over yonder, and there is water for your horses at the creek behind the house. My brother-in-law, James, is hunting with my two oldest boys. You will enjoy swapping tales with him shortly."

Elizabeth pointed in the direction of the various places, as she spoke.

Baron de Kalb nodded his thanks, and the young Marquis enthusiastically declared, "*Merci! Merci!*"

Turning to the kitchen, where she knew she would spend the rest of this day, Elizabeth realized once again that there was no guessing what a day would bring.

*****

Elizabeth's cooking had been enjoyed by all that evening, and conversations in both English and French had been exchanged with a deafening excitement around

81

the table and on the porch. Only crumbs were left of the hot biscuits and peach pies. There were only a few scraps of ham and chicken for the animals. Both her family and guests were now quite full of the bounteous meal.

Lafayette asked many questions about their lives and why the Hutchinsons, Jacksons, and Crawfords had come to America. After James explained the conditions in Scotland and how they had been treated there by the English, Lafayette spoke up.

"I was two when my Papa was killed fighting the English. He was a colonel and a great leader of men. When I understood about the war between our two countries, I decided that I, too, would fight them. Once I heard of your revolt, my heart was with you. *Maintenant*, I am here!

"My king, Louis XVI, did not wish me to leave France. My wife's parents, also, but my dear wife gave me her blessing. So, in spite of so much opposition, I bought *La Victorie* and found a captain for my ship. Hearing how farmers fought the British army, I knew my place was to fight with you.

"Disguising myself, I met my friend, Baron de Kalb, and we sailed from Spain for America. I am a trained soldier but have never fought. I must learn from General George Washington. He is a military leader, and he will teach me to be one.

"I wrote in a letter to my wife while on our ocean voyage: 'The welfare of America is intimately connected with the happiness of all mankind; she will become the respectable and safe asylum of virtue, integrity, tolerance, equality, and a peaceful liberty.' "

With his green eyes flashing, the gangling boy rose to his feet and lifted his tankard of cider, "*Vive* America! *Vive la France!*"

The other men, as well as the boys, stood and

followed his example. There was stomping of feet added to the loud voices. They toasted their countries and General Washington. The Americans toasted the French and vice versa. Many huzzahs were shouted in between, and a friendship was born in the Crawford house that night between men of different nationalities.

When the hullabaloo calmed, Elizabeth, still at her spinning wheel, asked the Marguis and the Baron, "Sirs, I have never visited the Lowcountry. What is it like?"

"We made landfall in the dead of night," began the Baron. "Monsieur Cantzon, it was a kind Huguenot like yourself that welcomed us to his plantation home; his name is Major Benjamin Huger. His hospitality greets us to your new country."

The young Lafayette interrupted, "*Mais, oui*, his three- year-old son Francis reminded me of myself as a boy. He carefully listened to the story of our adventure. Next, he challenged me to a sword fight with his wooden sword, and it was of great amusement. Madame Jackson, *je comprend* your sons will be warriors and defend their country. They have red hair like me, and we don't give up."

"Just like everyone in this household, my three sons are committed to the cause of liberty," stated Elizabeth emphatically. "We are passionate about defending what the good Lord has kindly given us."

"Major Huger sent us to Charlestown on his best horses, and the *Victorie,* our ship, met us there. There were tall trees along the road, and their limbs grew crookedly in different directions. Sometimes their branches met over the road to make a canopy of shade."

"Long, silver plants hung from the trees; they reminded me of the beards of old men. It was wispy when the wind caught it. My new friends in Charlestown gave me two names. The Indians call it tree hair, and the

French explorers named it Spanish Beard. We do not think highly of the Spanish, so I will call it Spanish Beard."

As he chuckled, Lafayette's eyes sparkled mischievously.

"The dirt is sandy, but it is the tiny insects that pierce and suck your blood that I detested. They are outside and inside, and they can bite through your clothing. What are those pestiferous insects?" questioned Lafayette.

"Aye," James guffawed. "When we built the fort at Sullivan's Island, some days I was sure those irritating mosquitoes would bite us to death before we had a chance to fight the British."

"The people we met in Charlestown were *tres agreeable*. They have built a pleasant and cosmopolitan city with its businesses, churches, the Exchange Building, a museum, and a theater and musical society. We left on June 25 to continue our journey to the camp of General Washington, but we enjoyed our stay."

The fifty-six-year-old Baron de Kalb added, "During the French and Indian War, I was sent as a spy here. I traveled extensively in all of the colonies, even yours, and am an experienced soldier. Your country is worth fighting for, and that is why I have returned.

"At every part of our journey, we have been welcomed. We have met strangers that have become friends over a meal cooked on an open fire or in a lovely home such as yours. *Merci beaucoup, Madame.*"

Lafayette stood and bowed graciously and with a flourish to Elizabeth.

"We have enjoyed hearing about your country and your heartfelt desire to help our country. We will pray for your safe travel as you continue on your way to meet with General Washington," said Elizabeth.

Elizabeth's oldest son, Hugh had listened

intently to the strangers' views on their fight for liberty and freedom from the British crown. He now practiced with the militia each month. He asked the Marquis, "Sir, I have heard that noble families have mottos to live by. What is yours?" "Cur non is the Lafayette motto. It means "why not?"

Anything is possible if you only try. King Louis XVI forbid me to come to America, but here I am." Elizabeth beamed at his words.

"Oh, sir! When I asked my husband Andrew why did he so desire to brave the dangers of traveling to America, he answered, 'Why not?' Like you, here we are!"

A Muster and A Farewell
June, 1779

One iron pot hung over the open fire, and the water was bubbling. The coals were red hot. Like most of the women around the militia field, Elizabeth arrived early that morning to build the cooking fire and surround it with large rocks from the stream. She had washed the pork twice to get rid of the excess salt. In the frying pan, she had browned the pork. Now it was time to add the bite-size pieces to the six pints of water.

Gathering the carrots and parsnips out of the woven basket beside her, Elizabeth also cut them into small chunks on the oak cutting board she had brought from home. After adding the vegetables, picked fresh from her garden that morning, salt, pepper, and apple cider vinegar were next. There would be another hour of simmering before it was time to add the cabbage, rosemary, and thyme.

Looking around at the other fires and smelling the various stews and soups, Elizabeth knew that each family would relish their meals this Saturday in early June,1779.

Sunshine filtered through the trees, and the morning fog had disappeared. Her moccasins were wet from the dew, so Elizabeth kicked them off. Hoping for some late berries, she spied some wild strawberry bushes to her right and headed in their direction.

The cadence of a drum interrupted her sightseeing, and she looked toward the field. It was Muster Day in the Waxhaws, and the church bell rang early this morning to call the men, young and old, to assemble. As the war had continued, the militia practiced more frequently. At one time, the muster call went out about every three months, but there were only weeks between calls now.

There was confusion aplenty on a day like today. The men and young boys drilled on the roped field, kept in line by the fife music and the shouted orders. The young carried long sticks over their shoulders, and the men carried their muskets. All the boys looked forward to owning their own rifles at age sixteen; it was an important rite of passage before joining the militia.

Sometimes a boy would inherit a family member's musket, and that was a treasure. Other times, a father would buy lock, stock, and barrel from a blacksmith. This weapon was not for hunting; it was a weapon of war. The Scotch-Irish had a high regard for civic duty, and these unpaid soldiers took protecting their families and land seriously.

Children of all ages played games and sang songs. They were singing "Yankee Doodle" as a round, laughing at the confusion of the words. After singing for awhile, they found a flat place for races with their hoops. Some of the boys had drawn a circle with a stick in the dirt and were playing marbles.

Elizabeth saw Robert and Andrew slinging their hatchets toward a tree. A stump was hanging from one of the lower branches as a target. Even though there was laughter among all the lads, the competition was evident. All wanted to strike in the center of the stump. The women cooked, visited with friends, and kept a watchful eye on everything.

Elizabeth and Nancy were still close friends, and they eagerly greeted each other with exuberant smiles. The widow of the beloved Reverend William Richardson had married George Dunlap. At age thirty-nine, Nancy was four months pregnant with her first child, and every day was an adventure for her.

"Elizabeth, I put on a pot of split pea stew with plenty of beef in it for George. I do believe he would be fine with only the meat and potatoes," said Nancy. "I brought left-over biscuits from last night. Why don't we put our meals together?"

"I truly would enjoy that! Last night I fried some cookies and rolled them in cinnamon sugar. Those should help that sweet tooth you have been fussing about," Elizabeth teased her friend.

A crowd of children, chanting as they walked, wandered by the two women, "Prime and load. Make ready. Present. Fire!" When they said prime and load, the children slapped their hips with their hands.

They had seen the militia hit their cartridge boxes to settle the gunpowder and mimicked the action, as well as the words.

They all shouted, "Fire!" at the top of their lungs.

Eerily, on the other side of the rope, a man's voice was next heard, "Prime and load. Make ready. Present. Fire!"

The earsplitting sound of gunfire seemed louder this time, and some of the men were temporarily obscured by smoke. The two women's eyes locked in surprise and dread of new possible horrors of this war for freedom; soldiers would disappear permanently in battle.

Twelve-year-old Andrew and Robert, the older by two years, ran up to their mother. Each carried a 4x4 block of wood.

"Look, Mamma, what that small bullet did to this piece of wood," Robert breathlessly said.

He showed Elizabeth one side of the board with four round holes along the middle, where the bullets entered. Then he excitedly turned it over and thrust it toward Elizabeth's face. On the other side was splintered wood and frayed edges around each hole where the bullet exited. In places, there was no circle at all. Elizabeth and Nancy both solemnly nodded their heads at the damage in front of them.

Holding up another piece of wood, Andrew pushed in front of his brother. Turning it sideways, Andrew eagerly showed them more destruction from other bullets. These bullets had only grazed the wood, rather than hitting it head-on. Fragments hung from the side, and the pieces were split in strips.

"Those sorry British and Tories best watch out for our marksmanship," Andrew exclaimed. "The bullets may only be the size of a marble, but they can do powerful damage.

"Uncle James explained that the spin of the rifle balls in the gun barrel make them more accurate. I heard him tell Hugh that at twenty-five yards, the exit holes are bigger in the back than in the front."

Robert interrupted, "Now we know why it is critical to put enough gunpowder in the cartridge. We want those bullets to find their marks."

Nancy put both her arms around her unborn baby and prayed for its safety.

Elizabeth swallowed hard before she spoke to her sons.

"Aye, the more you know about how to defend yourselves the happier I will be. I am glad your uncle continues to teach you about surviving in a war. Having a healthy respect for your weapons, and the enemies, is vital."

"Come on, Robert, let's work on that stump some more with our hatchets. Even a tool might save our lives one day," encouraged Andrew.

With troubled sighs and wrinkled brows, both women turned back to the field to watch their loved ones prepare for war. Elizabeth's eyes quickly sought out her oldest son Hugh in the midst of a line, marching and turning to the drum signals of Alexander, the young drummer.

Alex was a boy about the same age as Andrew, and Elizabeth watched that drummer's father obey the signals of his son. War turned a family upside down, and Elizabeth doubted her family would be immune in the coming days.

Elizabeth turned to Nancy and said, "Do you see that small knapsack Alex has?"

"Aye," Nancy replied. "Is that where he carries the cat-o-nine-tails? 'Tis horrified I was to learn that a mere boy would have that responsibility! For truth, it might even be used on him if he is derelict in his duties."

"James said that when he was in Charlestown that some of the older men teased their drummer boy by saying, 'Don't let the cat out of the bag,'" shared Elizabeth.

Shaking her head at that news, Nancy observed, "The obligations of children and adults are nearly the same in our world. Perchance, in another day childhood will be longer."

Both women turned back to their viewing, as loud huzzahs filled the air. The group practicing their marksmanship were proud of their shots at the target.

The militia was a motley group. Some were in buckskins, and others wore broad-brimmed hats and homespun shirts. Moccasins were on some feet, and leather boots covered others. Many were barefoot.

Their equipment was not uniform either. A variety of rifles, muskets, and fowling pieces were balanced on their shoulders, as they awaited the next command. Their secondary weapons, hatchets, or knives, were readily available to each man. The hatchets hung by ropes tied to their belts, and small knives were sheathed in their boots.

Cartridge boxes and powder horns were full.

Elizabeth and Nancy strolled among the watching crowd toward the fifer practicing at the lower corner of the field. They spoke to other watching mothers and wives as they went. All were focused on the militia's preparations.

Skirmishes with the British all over the colony had awakened the Upcountry to the British plans to move their fight into the South, and defense preparations were required immediately.

Samuel Knox, the fifer, continued to practice, even with an audience. Children danced to his playing, and various women clapped their hands to the rhythms. The piercing sound of the fife could not be ignored, and it woke the men with "Reveille" and "Tattoo" sent them to bed. The fifer's duty compelled him to be the first to wake in the morning and the last to go to bed. His fife, carved out of a single piece of wood with six holes in it, wielded power over the days of men.

The drummer and the fifer were noncombatants, so they carried no weapons, but they were indispensable to every military group. The musicians provided directions on a march, during a battle, and within a campsite. Besides transmitting orders, they also determined the time of daily signals for a camp.

Elizabeth looked over at the trees close to the field. She saw younger boys hunkered down and running from tree to tree. Using the same tactics of guerrilla warfare that their fathers did during a battle, the children pretended to evade an unseen enemy.

Many obscure hand signals, as well as hands raised to follow, were obvious through the leaves. One boy made it a point of sliding from tree to tree on his belly. He was covered from head to foot with the red dust of the Waxhaws, but his smile of white teeth shone through the shadows. He was most pleased with his dashing sprints.

Elizabeth turned to Nancy, as they walked back to the campfires.

The aromas of sweet-smelling food summoned them.

"Children didn't play war games in Ireland. We played Duck, Duck, Goose and hide-and-seek most afternoons. Those games were all about running and catching and hiding and finding."

Nancy softly continued, "Children playing. Meals cooking. Nothing to do with war at all."

At that precise moment, the loud firing of rifles cut short their pensive thoughts. Those sounds of reality won out.

*****

Because the war in Carolina had claimed the attention of the Waxhaws community, the muster of that Saturday was only a memory.

Barely two days later, Elizabeth watched Hugh eat the massive breakfast she had cooked. Besides the fried eggs her eldest son loved so much, Elizabeth had baked the oat bannock cakes in plenty of butter, so the round bread could easily be cut in triangles and turned out on the pewter platter. There was cider, cold or hot, on the warm June morning. Hugh chose the cold.

Rather than only have the pork from the night before, Elizabeth fried chicken for breakfast, too. It was another one of Hugh's favorites, and her purpose for this meal was all about spoiling her sixteen-year-old.

Hugh was leaving at daybreak to ride with other Waxhaws militia volunteers under Captain Robert Crawford, the older brother of his Uncle James. James was sending one of his wagons to haul supplies in, in addition to two of his sons. Robert and Andy were both jealous of their older brother's journey that morning.

"Hugh, do you have plenty of cartridges? What will you do if you run out?" asked Andy.

Deliberately biting again into his fried chicken leg before he answered, Hugh replied, "It depends on how much action we see before we come home. Reckon I have plenty to spare."

Hugh shrugged casually.

Elizabeth turned slowly to look intently into Hugh's face. Confidence was a good trait, but cockiness was not. His blue eyes squarely met her blue ones, and she nodded her approval.

The mother's stomach was in knots, and the hot tea had not helped. Walking briskly around the table, she nervously rearranged the dishes and patted Hugh's shoulder. Unshed tears left over from the night before stayed in place. Elizabeth wanted Hugh to remember her smile, not her tears.

"Don't ever give up, Hugh, even if your shot runs out! Remember our grandfather Jackson and the other local militia at the Battle of Carrickfergus. After five days, those French troops finally gave up and left Ireland. The British soldiers here in Carolina will do the same, because we won't give up either!" exclaimed Robert.

"Huzzah! Huzzah! Huzzah!" shouted the men in the Caldwell keeping room, as they all stood to their feet.

The tankards of cider were raised to the ceiling, and fists pounded on the trestle table. Even the dogs howled or barked, and that added to the din. Elizabeth had added the red scarf to Hugh's pack. He had complained for two days about a sore throat. Even though it was June, that scarf might feel pleasant around his neck.

Elizabeth was standing by the door by now. Out of the corner of her eye she saw dirt flying as horses galloped up the road. Colonel William Richardson Davie, the nephew of the late Reverend Richardson, stood tall in the saddle, as he led the mounted company.

Goodbyes were brief, and Hugh fell in with other young men in the line of horses. He raised his arm and waved in farewell, straightened his back, and looked ahead to a battle with the British soldiers intent on taking his land away.

A Special Visit
October, 1779

Even in October, soap making was hot work. Elizabeth wiped her brow with the end of the red scarf tied around her waist. The weather was a bit cooler than in the spring, and soap was needed now for the household. She was using the available pork and beef fat from the fall butchering.

Every day for the past two months, she had scooped up the cold ashes after raking them to the front of the fireplace. She would sift through them to be sure there were no stray, burning embers. Pouring the ashes into a bucket several times a day, Elizabeth would carry the full tin bucket to the stable at night and empty the ashes into a barrel. Saving the ashes was the first step to soap making.

To keep the ashes dry, the barrel stood inside the open door of the stable. The barrel was about five feet deep and lined with straw. It had a false bottom made out of lattice, and there was a drain near the bottom that was plugged with a wooden peg.

Elizabeth and Nancy Richardson Dunlop were helping each other make a supply of soap for the next few months. It was exhausting work, and Nancy was now seven months pregnant. Elizabeth was making sure she spelled Nancy often to give her back a rest.

It was day two, and already both women were experiencing muscle pains that weren't evident the day before.

Nancy sat down on stump with a sigh.

"Gracious me! My babe is loudly protesting this task. I declare there seems to be somersaulting and kicking going on!"

The first-time mother laughed, as she hugged

her stomach.

"Elizabeth, that looks like Margaret headed our way," Nancy spoke in between giggles.

Elizabeth waved at the wagon coming quickly around the curve. It was Margaret McKemie, Elizabeth's older sister.

Running toward the wagon, Elizabeth broke into a smile of excitement at seeing her sister. Because of sickness in Margaret's family, it had been several weeks since they had seen each other.

Margaret hollered to the dappled gray mare pulling the small wagon, "Whoa, Beck. Whoa, girl."

The horse slowed and then stopped, nodding its mane in obedience.

Climbing off the seat, Margaret smiled brightly at her younger sister "I need a hug from you, my bonny girl. Do you remember how Mother always called us bonny girls? I would dearly love to hear her voice today! But I am most glad to be spending the day with you and Nancy," declared Margaret.

"It appears to me that another pair of hands will be welcome," nodding kindly to Nancy. "So, let's get this chore completed until next time."

The two sisters walked arm-in-arm toward the open fire where the steam floating above the kettle attested to its rising temperature.

"I wish I had that bar of soap I brought with me on the ship. I never knew what a luxury it was until it washed away after only three weeks. It disappeared too soon," reflected Elizabeth.

"I remember Mother crying once when it was time to make soap. But she soon dried her tears and decided that being clean and having fresh clothes was worth the hard work," said Nancy.

"It didn't take her long to perfect her timing of the cooking either. She would sporadically stop to see if the stir-stick could stand up by itself. When that stick could stand upright, the gooey mess had cooked aplenty."

Elizabeth checked the lye water falling out of the drain into the bucket. The clear rainwater had performed its work as it changed the consistency of the ashes. Color was the secret to the ashes being ready.

"The lye is the perfect brownish color," she revealed. "Perchance it is time to pour the lye water into the fat and commence to stir this smelly mixture."

All three women had made personal reactions to the smell of the cooking fat. Nancy was feeling squeamish and took deep breaths. Margaret periodically raised a handkerchief of lavender to her face, and Elizabeth regularly held her breath because of the pungent smell; this task was one for the outdoors.

It was now October, almost four months since the Battle of Stono Ferry near Charlestown on June 20. As she stirred the mixture with the long paddle, she made sure to keep her long skirts away from the hot coals. The open fire was a hazard that could quickly turn to disaster, and even death, if the sparks suddenly reached the edges of clothes. Nancy and Margaret chatted in the background, but Elizabeth's thoughts were soon elsewhere.

Elizabeth shook her head as the memories of hearing about her oldest son's death came flying back into her consciousness. Her fingers twitched on the paddle.

*****

The morning was clear that June day, and she was spinning wool thread on the porch when she heard the horse's hoofs in the distance.

Looking toward the sound with expectancy, she

recognized first the horse that her nephew, William Crawford, rode. His horse was the only black horse around, with those distinctive white legs.

Elizabeth pushed back from the wheel and stood up. By the time Thomas reached the porch, she was on the top step. She was sure he had news of the militia; maybe Hugh and the rest were not far behind.

Word had already reached the farm about the Battle of Stono Ferry and how the attack on the Loyalist garrison had failed.

As William rode into the yard, Elizabeth could clearly see the hurt and anger in his face. His eyes were locked on hers, and he jumped off his horse.

Wobbling a bit, Elizabeth grabbed the porch post. Thomas reached out his arms to her, and goosebumps traveled up her arms. His face spoke before his mouth opened.

"Aunt Elizabeth, it's Hugh. He's not with us; we buried him near Charlestown."

Elizabeth plopped down hard on the steps and crossed her arms, as if to ward off the words about her eldest son. William took a deep breath and sat beside her, putting his arm around her shoulders. He had to tell the whole story.

"We knew Hugh was feeling poorly when we left. He kept that red scarf wrapped around his throat, even during the hot days. Every time I asked him about turning back, he only grinned and straightened his shoulders. At night, we bunked beside each other, and for two nights I heard his teeth chattering from chills and fever before we reached the Stono River. He coughed continuously, but he never faltered on his horse or on that battle advance.

"We were twelve miles west of Charlestown when we reached the ferry. General Lincoln's troops were stopped by the cannons and musket fire. The militia kept pressing, but finally retreated. The orders came for us to break camp early on June 20, and we marched toward the garrison at 7:00 in the morning.

"I stayed close to Hugh, knowing that the first time in battle is a fearful spot. Even though I am seventeen years older than he, Hugh has always been like a younger brother to me.

"Hugh stood tall, Aunt Elizabeth. Even though his face was red with fever, he didn't quit. He loaded and fired his rifle at our enemies without faltering. He has always been a sharpshooter when hunting, and he proved it that day. He obeyed orders and never wavered in his duty.

From the morning when we left here, Hugh was focused on fighting the British and protecting our homes. I was proud of your son; he never wavered in being the kind of soldier any man would be proud to fight beside."

Elizabeth listened intently to William's words without interrupting. When he stopped, she turned to him and forced herself not to shudder at his news.

"Where was he wounded, William?" she questioned.

She had to know immediately what hurt and killed her oldest son.

"Oh, Aunt Elizabeth, he wasn't shot. It was his illness that took him to Heaven.

"After the battle that afternoon, he started throwing up and complained of a powerful headache. He kept holding his head with both hands, as if to keep his head from exploding. He was dizzy and couldn't walk without help. Rather than being flushed with fever, he lost all color in his face. I tried to get him to drink water, but he couldn't swallow. Then he lost consciousness and seemed to rest. In only a wee time, he breathed his last.

"The surgeon tried bleeding him, but it did nary

a bit of good. There was one other peculiar symptom that I noticed. Hugh didn't sweat those last two days. The heat was sweltering, and I dripped sweat at times. The heat was powerful close, and all of us complained. I tied a cloth around my forehead to keep my eyes clear, but it appeared to not bother Hugh."

Out of his knapsack, William pulled the unwashed red scarf that Elizabeth had knitted for Hugh and handed it to her.

Elizabeth grabbed it, clapped it to her heart, and buried her head into it. The loss of her son Hugh crushed her heart. Her loud keening splintered the air.

Just as Elizabeth had clutched it that June day when she heard the news, she once again gripped the red scarf tied around her waist. It was becoming tattered from so much wear and tear, but the scarf brought Hugh close to her, and she couldn't explain why. Elizabeth continued to stir the mixture that would soon be soap.

Again, sounds of travelers interrupted Elizabeth's reverie.

Looking over her shoulder, Elizabeth saw the wagons of their friend, Traugott Bagge. She broke into a bright smile and waved to him.

"Margaret and Nancy, our Moravian friends are here!" exclaimed Elizabeth. "Margaret, the soap is most complete. Will you spell me to stir for just this last bit?"

Margaret took Elizabeth's place and pushed her sister toward the wagons. She had noted the woeful face on Elizabeth, as she stirred the soap, and was delighted to see the sorrow turn to gladness. Surprise company was clearly a good thing to send the doldrums off.

An hour later, the soap was fluffy, and the paddle stood straight up in the mixture; the soft soap had cooked enough. Margaret put out the fire and covered the pot.

The hot mixture had to cool for at least a day

before it was poured into a wooden barrel. Then the brown, jelly-like, and slippery substance would be foamy when mixed with water.

The barrel was handy for all in the kitchen. Hanging on the side of the barrel would be a gourd for dipping the soft soap out whenever it was needed.

*****

From the abundant supply of apples packed in the straw, the three women had worked together to make three, large apple pies. There was room on the table to mix and roll out the crusts. Each one routinely put a crust in the bottom of the crockery dishes and then added a layer of ripe apples, pared and sliced thin. Sugar was next, enough to cover the apples. The filling alternated with apples and sugar until the dish was full. All three women reached for the common spices of cinnamon and ground cloves in the bottles nearby.

Margaret and Nancy started to place the top crust on their pies and stopped when they saw Elizabeth reach for a small bottle and sprinkle a few teaspoons on her pie. The familiar scent of summer spread in the air.

Margaret immediately exclaimed, "Is that rose water, Elizabeth?"

With a smile, Elizabeth nodded, "When my roses were dying out this summer, I remembered Mother used to make rose water from the fresh petals. I have been experimenting with it and using it for a seasoning. I like its sweet-smelling freshness."

Nancy held out her hand for the bottle, sprinkled the rose water on her pie, and handed the bottle to Margaret.

"Methinks that all our pies should be the same," remarked Nancy, as she covered the fruit in her pan.

As the women cleaned up the table, so they

101

could all sit around it to eat, the appetizing aroma of the pies wafted outside the door to the porch where the men were sitting.

In an hour, Elizabeth called the men inside. There was a rush to be the first through the small door.

Elizabeth, Margaret, and Nancy sat at the long table with Robert, Andy, and James. Elizabeth had rung the porch bell to tell the others that company had arrived. Traugott Bagge and his workers also gathered with the family.

Elizabeth had made coffee from the recipe that Traugott had shared with her several years before. Each mug was filled with the hot liquid mixed with sugar and milk.

Before they ate, James asked Traugott to bless the food with the Moravian blessing his family used.

All at the table held hands, as Traugott said, "Come, Lord Jesus, our Guest to be, and bless these gifts bestowed by Thee. Bless our loved ones everywhere. And keep them in Thy tender care. Amen."

James then asked about his market trip to Charlestown. Eagerly the Moravian recalled what he had seen.

"Merchants were glad to see me, a tad more than usual, it appeared to me. We sold all the beeswax candles this time, except for the package I brought you, Elizabeth."

"The small businesses remained open during their regular hours, and families strolled on the battery. Countless sea gulls circled the spires of both St. Michael's and St. Philip's. Ships regularly navigated in and out of the harbor. Seamen raucously walked the streets, as ladies rode in their carriages. Sea breezes brought the ocean into the town, so the sights and smells of the port city remained alike to my last visit."

The Moravian merchant, Traugott, paused and

thoughtfully continued.

"At first glance, the city appears unaffected by the war. Bystanders talked about a possible attack by the Continental Army on Savannah. Soldiers in small groups patrolled during the day and night. I saw women look over their shoulders at possible danger, but nothing that was visible. Even though their children protested, mothers tightly held their hands. The men carried both their pistols and rifles in full view."

"Charlestown is a city in waiting, like a mother awaiting her child."

Nodding to Nancy, Traugott turned to Janes and continued. "Yes, we Moravians are pacifists and don't serve as soldiers, but we, too, believe in the liberty to worship as we so desire. We consider our religious choice to be a freedom that all men and women should enjoy. Our members had to meet secretly in Europe for almost a century because of persecution."

Looking then to Elizabeth, he continued, "Elizabeth, you have suffered a mighty blow from the war with the loss of your oldest son. He was a fine young man, and I admired his courage as a soldier."

Elizabeth struggled to remain composed at his kind words, but some tears trickled down her cheeks. Margaret reached for her younger sister's hands and gently clasped them in her own.

"Our town of Salem was dedicated to God and the service of our fellowman. Every day we meet as a family for meditations, prayers, and the singing of hymns. We cherish each member of our kin, and I know your sons are a treasure to you.

"James, your hospitality has graciously welcomed us on many occasions into your home. In our faith, we observe a love feast on special occasions. It is a time of celebrating fellowship and hospitality together. May we celebrate a love feast together this day with your family? We have already started it with this simple repast of the delicious pie and our coffee recipe. Often we only have a small sweet with the coffee."

Traugott's voice was excited at the prospect of sharing this Moravian custom with his friends.

"Aye," James swiftly answered. "It would be a good way to end this day."

Pulling his Daily Text out of his knapsack, Traugott found the printed words of the day and read, "Our watchword for this week is 'Commit your way to the Lord; trust in Him, and He will act.' Psalm 37:5."

He looked around the table and explained, "We have a Bible verse for each week that we focus on. Then for each day, we read one verse from the Old Testament and one from the New Testament.

"'Genesis 28:15 says, 'Know that I am with you and will keep you wherever you go.'"

"'By faith Abraham obeyed when he was called to set out for a place that he was to receive as an inheritance: and he set out, not knowing where he was going.' Hebrews 11:8."

"James, will you now pray for us?" finished Traugott.

"Lord, our Rock, help us to be steadfast in faith and continue to trust You that Your plan for us is perfect. We thank you for this land of promise that You gave us, and we work hard to take good care of it. Now we are fighting for it, and we ask your guidance. This revolution has already cost our family with Hugh's life, and we mourn his loss. Give us strength to continue to battle the strong English army that is our foe. You are our Comforter, and we thank you for walking both the easy and the hard roads with us. Thank you especially today for our Moravian friends and thank you for every visit with them that we enjoy. In Jesus' name, amen," responded James.

104

The whole table eyed Traugott expectantly to see what was next.

"And now, Irvin, will you fetch the box of spare candles from my wagon?"

The young man speedily made his way to the wagon and back to the table. There were small candles in the box, and a red ribbon was tied around each one.

Traugott took the box to each one at the table for them to choose a candle. After all the Crawford/ Jackson family and the Moravian guests held one, Traugott went to the fireplace to light his candle. Then he went to each person to light their candles from his. The light of dusk was fading, and the candles lighted the keeping room with a soft glow. It was surprising how those small candles created a bond that was special and unusual between the individuals.

Looking around the table, Elizabeth noted her sons' faces wreathed in the candlelight and whispered a heart-felt thank you for her two youngest.

"Now we shall sing together "Now Thank We All Our God." Let us stand and lift our candles high," instructed Traugott.

Now thank we all our God, with heart and hands and voices, Who wondrous things has done, in Whom this world rejoices; Who from our mothers' arms has blessed us on our way With countless gifts of love, and still is ours today.

Oh, may this bounteous God through all our life be near us, With ever joyful hearts and blessed peace to cheer us; And keep us in His grace, and guide us when perplexed; And guard us through all ills in this world, till the next! All praise and thanks to God the Father now be given,

The Son and Him Who reigns with Them in highest
Heaven; The one eternal God,
Whom earth and Heav'n adore;
For thus it was, is now, and shall be evermore.

The simple Moravian custom, shared with this family of Presbyterians, connected the two religions in a bond that gave hope for the unknown future of a country at war.

A Desolate Spring Day
May, 1780

Ordinary sights and sounds of the forest flooded the Camden-Salisbury Road. The air was filled with birds and bird songs. A menagerie of spring fauna made their afternoon excursions. A doe followed by her fawn leapt over the fallen tree. A red tail hawk silently swooped toward the uneven red clay to grab an unsuspecting field mouse. Even the newborn bunnies were hopping awkwardly around their mother.

It was Monday, May 29, 1780, when military sounds interrupted this warm and sultry spring day.

First came a caravan of supply wagons and field artillery. Some wagons were drawn by four horses and others by two. Strapped down in the covered baggage wagons were medicine chests, tents, and officers' gear. Foodstuffs were also in covered wagons, and the various barrels of hard tack, potatoes, corn, and dried and salted beef were tightly packed. In between the casks were iron cooking pots and skillets, tin kettles, axes, and wooden cooking utensils. Another set of wagons carried extra rifles and muskets, sturdy barrels of gunpowder, and lead bricks to make bullets. Two six-pounder cannons on caissons brought up the rear.

Shouts from the wagoners and the crack of whips encouraged the horses forward.

In the midst of the wagons rode the advanced guard. These wagons were essential to the livelihood of the 3rd. Virginia Regiment of Colonel Abraham Buford. Since the fall of Charlestown to the British on May 12, his men were the last Continental troops in the South. They had been ordered to retreat to Hillsborough, North Carolina and await orders.

It was barely three o'clock when those military

sounds of wagons and troops turned into the sounds of battle and bloodshed.

As they scrambled through the underbrush in the woods, Elizabeth and her two sons stayed close to the tree coverage. They, along with many others from the community, watched 53 prisoners secured with knotted rope by the enemy.

Hidden behind low limbs close to the scene, Elizabeth stuffed her fist into her mouth to keep from screaming in horror at the carnage both on the road and in the woods.

A few hand-to-hand fights continued, but British officers gradually gained control of their men. The ringing sounds of steel against steel slowly diminished.

The wounded soldiers of Colonel Abraham Buford's Virginia Continentals lay at the mercy of the unforgiving bayonets and sabers of Lieutenant Colonel Banastre Tarleton's British Legion cavalry, British Legion infantry, and Seventeenth Light Dragoons. There were no cries for mercy from the injured, only struggles to roll away from the deadly weapons and shrieks of pain.

Robert turned away and vomited in the grass, and Andy furiously pounded a tree trunk in frustration, wishing it wore a green jacket.

The nightmare continued, and some of the women covered their eyes or turned away. Mothers grabbed their children's heads and forced them to look away from the massacre. Sadly, all ears were unplugged, and tears freely flowed down those same faces.

113 American soldiers and 5 British soldiers lay dead; In fifteen minutes,150 Patriots and 14 English soldiers lay wounded from their injuries.

Silently the women and children backed away from the desolate scene to fetch wagons to move the wounded to their meeting house.

Along with others, Elizabeth, Robert, and Andy, marched toward the bodies and screams to give aid.

Draped over the bodies and the ground was smoke from the rifles and muskets. The fog of war obscured the scene's reality until Elizabeth stumbled over the first body.

Elizabeth knew that others had nursed her son Hugh the year before, and those memories compelled her forward into the confusion. She took the place of the wives and mothers of the crumpled men at this crossroads, only steps away from her home.

Kneeling first beside a tall, young man of twenty-five and staring intently at his many wounds, Elizabeth instantly knew he was dead. A deathblow had almost severed his head from his body. Still clutched tightly in his right hand was his infantry captain's sword. It had a buckhorn handle mounted heavily in silver. Elizabeth read his name carved into the handle – Adam Wallace.

Reaching over to shut his eyes, Elizabeth whispered, "My thanks to you, Captain Adam Wallace. Ye fought hard this day, and I admire your courage."

Another young soldier beside the captain murmured, "Water, missus, please."

Andy gulped, swallowed hard, and then stepped around his mother to unhook the man's wooden canteen from his belt. The thirteen-year-old held the soldier's head up, so he could drink without choking. Still the water spilled out of the chapped lips, but little was lost.

Elizabeth intently gave orders to her sons.

"Sons, the men need water in this heat. Water could save their lives. Go among them and share water from their canteens as needed. Use your knives to cut bandages from their shirts, and then press that cloth tight to their wounds. It will help stop the bleeding.

"I will be right here with you, and we can help

109

many together. I pray many more hands will be here soon, but we must hurry. Time is critical to saving their lives now; we can't tarry!"

Elizabeth tempered her instructions with a reassuring smile and turned to the next soldier. There was no time to waste because some voices were fainter. She closed her ears to the moans and cries as she moved from one soldier to another.

As Robert and Andy stepped to and fro among the soldiers, Elizabeth was proud that neither shrank from the horrors before them.

Soon wagons driven by women and older children were at the scene, and the hurt and cut bodies were carried to the wagons.

Nancy called to Elizabeth from her loaded wagon.

"Elizabeth, we will take them to the meeting house. Others have taken hay to put on the floor to soften the surface."

Her words trembled at the end, and Nancy choked back a sob. She tightened her grip on the reins and looked hard once again at the scene of fallen soldiers. Nancy knew the imprint of this picture was fixed on her heart, as well as her mind.

It would have been easier to walk away and try to forget the ghastly scene. None of the women had experienced war, but their hard-set faces revealed their determination to not turn away.

Reverend Jacob Carnes came running into the confusion, along with some other local men, and halted in his tracks. Looking and listening to all the suffering, his anguished, but loud and confident voice, suddenly reached through the moans. He walked among the fallen, as he spoke.

The Lord is my shepherd; I shall not want.

He maketh me to lie down in green pastures:
He leadeth me beside the still waters.
He restoreth my soul:
He leadeth me in the paths of righteousness
 for his name's sake.
Yea, though I walk through the valley of the shadow of
death, I will fear no evil:
for thou art with me;
thy rod and thy staff they comfort me.
Thou preparest a table before me in the presence of mine
enemies:
thou anointest my head with oil;
my cup runneth over.
Surely goodness and mercy shall follow me all the days
of my life: and I will dwell in the house of the Lord
forever.

Men stifled their groans, wanting desperately to
hear the Words quoted by the minister. Some shut their
eyes to their maimed bodies to focus on the Bible
promises. As the afternoon sun gleamed through the
trees, other soldiers peered through the branches, seeking
the light.

Elizabeth staunched the blood from one soldier's
severed hand, and his gaze locked with her eyes.

He softly joined his shaky voice with Reverend
Carnes, "...and I will dwell in the house of the Lord
forever."

"Aye, young man, that we will," she tenderly
replied, as she brushed his hair back from his face.
Elizabeth forced herself not to shudder at the wreckage
to his body.

"Now, here come some strong arms that will lift
you to the wagons. Perchance, we will talk later at our
meeting house. You will be more comfortable there."

Lead shot littered the ground where Elizabeth

was, and some was still hot to the touch. She kicked it away from the men with her moccasins. Muskets were gripped in hands or leaned against other bodies. Some cartridge boxes hung from nearby branches. More shoes were off the soldiers' feet rather than on.

As Elizabeth moved closer to where her own sons were, she heard orders shouted at those British soldiers, standing or sitting at ease.

"Look lively, men! Go grab a shovel or an ax. A mass grave needs to be dug. We will bury both our enemies and our fellow soldiers together in the same place. A shallow ditch will do."

"Digging in this red clay will quickly make new muscles for ye. Your sweethearts will be glad of this work you do today. Head for that patch of grass to the right of this road. No lollygagging now," directed Major Charles Cochrane of the British Legion Infantry.

Gritting her teeth at the callous-sounding words, Elizabeth covered the still face of a brown-haired young man whose deathblows were from sabers, not bullets. As she looked around at the bodies, slowly she realized that most had died from brutal cuts. Moving the injured soldiers had converted slashes into wide slices, and already the green grass was turning brown.

Elizabeth's hair fell from her cap, but she didn't notice. Not realizing either that tears streamed down her face, Elizabeth crawled from one-to-another until she was beside both Robert and Andy.

Inching between the two, she hugged each one, as if she had not seen them in weeks. The boys were startled at first by their mother. But then her words gave them quick understanding of the embrace.

"I love ye, my sons. I am most proud of your actions this day." A red-haired man lying in front of Andy was wildly talking, and Elizabeth held his hand to quiet him.

"Ensign Cruit carried high our white flag of surrender toward the Green Dragoons, and he was shot!"

The wounded man gasped for air and continued. "I saw him sway and jerk before he allowed the flag to fall to the ground. Even his horse was shot down. Under orders, we had grounded our arms. The firing began in earnest from our enemy, and then their cavalry charged."

A second soldier took up their horrific story while tightly holding his ribcage.

"They came at us with their swords and bayonets raised above their heads, and I smelt the rat. Now I can't move my leg, and I see holes oozing blood from those cursed bayonets."

He groaned and heaved a sigh before he spoke again.

"I could tell no difference in the screams. Whether we were on the ground or trying to hold our hands up in surrender, our shrieks mingled with our attackers. Until at last our assailants completed their foul business."

Robert and Andy's eyes opened wide. They knew the rules of honor in war: a flag of surrender, the throwing down of weapons, or the raising of arms were plain signs to an enemy.

"The British gave you no mercy; they continued to attack you?" cried Robert. "Who commanded the British against you? I warrant his officer's training needs repeating!"

The red-haired soldier answered, "Lieutenant Colonel Banastre Tarleton."

"Mayhap his name will be remembered again," alleged Andy. "That white flag was clearly a request of clemency, but he and his soldiers refused you. Our soldiers will nary forget the actions of Tarleton's Quarter."

Two English infantry pushed past the small

113

group and picked up the body of one of the Virginia Continentals. A hat fell off his head, and his rifle was left on the ground. The mass grave completed, and now the dead were being moved to their final resting place.

"We can't help them, but we can relieve the suffering of those around us, sons," reminded Elizabeth. "I see another empty wagon. These men need their wounds tended to, and they need to be under shelter.

"A soldier over there keeps biting down tightly on a bullet trying to control his pain, and I must needs go to him. I cannot watch him clench his rifle with those white knuckles any longer. I will meet you later at the meeting house."

She was stopped in her tracks by a hand grabbing her skirts.

"Ma'am, I didn't have time to load again. We only shot one volley, and then they were on us. They attacked from all sides. I didn't have time," his voice trailed off in misery.

Then he shut his eyes.

Elizabeth stood still to catch her breath from the surrounding tragedy. She continued to step over other bodies and knelt beside the man who had captured her eyes.

"My name is Elizabeth Jackson, sir, and I am here to help you until others can take you to a safer place only two miles away."

The man was bleary-eyed from his obvious pain, but he raised his own left hand to take the bullet out of his mouth. His right hand was nowhere to be seen.

Without waiting for him to answer, Elizabeth untied the cording from her pocket and tied it around his arm for a tourniquet. He had lost a lot of blood. While she worked, the soldier sluggishly recounted his misfortunes.

"I am Captain John Stokes, ma'am, and I reckon

am no longer hale and hearty, as I was," John pondered that thought for a moment.

"It appears you have many wounds, John," gently observed Elizabeth. "Most have stopped bleeding."

"We were in one line when they reached us. Even though we knelt with our hands in the air in surrender, they slashed at all of us."

John shivered at the visual the words brought back to his mind.

"I recollect that two British dragoons attacked me with their sabers. I had my hand above my head for protection, and a slash took it off. Next, I lost a finger on my left hand before I was thrown to the ground with a blow to my head."

"Seems like I am still dizzy from that blow," he continued, as he shut his eyes to stop the spinning.

"I reeled from all the pain and staggered into other men who were suffering, too. There was no escape, and every second I knew I was going to Heaven. One man with a bayonet offered to finish me off, but I still survived. And here I am, and I don't know why."

As John talked, Elizabeth had counted the wounds on his mangled body. Besides the loss of his hand and a forefinger on his left hand, the soldier had over twenty slashes and punctures.

Elizabeth smiled at him, smoothed his furrowed brow, and rose to her feet.

She tried to let her mind wander as she continued her rounds on the battlefield, but she was already single-minded that too much listening kept her from helping the injured others.

Determined to smile and sing softly to herself as if she were doing her daily chores appeared a better choice. Each soldier needed encouragement and hope, not tears from a nurse. And though outwardly she appeared a picture of serenity, inside she was beginning to steal herself for what would come next.

She knew that after today, she and her sons would be unwavering to do whatever it took to put an end to this struggle for freedom no matter what the cost.

Standing and Fighting Together 1780

Elizabeth feverously knitted to complete the second scarf. The rhythmic tapping of her wooden needles and the crackling fire were the only sounds in the quiet household this dark, summer night. This indigo scarf, nearly finished in her lap, was for Andy; the yellow one for Robert lay crumpled at her feet. Elizabeth crafted these two from the same design as Hugh's red scarf. They were identical except for their colors.

The mother had almost worn-out Hugh's red scarf since he died last year. With her wearing it every day, she had to frequently reknit sections. She whispered prayers of protection for her sons, as she worked. She had seen the mercy of British and Tory troops on the battlefield two months ago in May. Elizabeth had nursed those poor soldiers with the hacked limbs.

Remembering those horrific wounds, Elizabeth prayed and spoke the words of the psalmist David over her sons, "I have made You my dwelling place, the Most High who is my refuge and I trust that because of this no evil shall be allowed to befall me, no plague come near my home. For He will command His angels concerning me to guard me (and my boys) in all our ways. In Jesus' name, Amen."

Elizabeth took a deep breath, straightened her back, and resolutely focused once again on the task at hand.

The light from the fireplace and the candle was dim, but Elizabeth was accustomed to carrying out most of her daily tasks at night. The faint glow was sufficient. Even the tears that trickled down her cheeks and blurred her vision didn't slow her down.

Since the Battle of Waxhaws, Robert and Andy

had been practicing their riflery every day. Robert had become quite the sharpshooter, and Andy improved daily. Although they whined constantly of sore shoulders where the rifle stocks kicked after firing, they were equally persistent at their training. Even during the summer storms in June, the two brothers ran in the woods from tree to tree, mimicking the drill of the militia.

Uncle James was lending a hand in training their two marsh tackies to not shy away from gunfire or other horses in the hullabaloo of an attack. The sure-footed mounts kept pace with their owners in preparation for how to handle the clamor and mayhem of a battle.

Shouts, gunfire, and careening horses could be simulated, but there was no planning for the anguish and blood of actual combat.

As he walked over the threshold into the keeping room, James stumbled and then quickly caught his balance.

"Tis still wet from the night dew, but the wind has blown the storm clouds away. It will be fair and muggy as they ride out. Appears you have been working by the fire all night, Elizabeth? That coffee smells agreeable. Shall I pour us a cup?"

"Aye, that will get me moving toward fixing our breakfast," Elizabeth replied, as she bound the stitches off on the last row of the blue scarf.

She stretched her arms up to the rafters to relieve the tightness in her shoulders. Typically, a night of stitchery was a relaxing one. But with her sons riding out this morning with Major William Richardson Davie's militia, Elizabeth had tasted fear all night.

When James handed her the cup of steaming coffee, Elizabeth smiled and nodded her thanks. Her unwavering blue eyes confidently met his firm brown eyes, and James raised his cup in salute to her solid faith.

"This is our country, Elizabeth, and we are going to fight to hold it. This is my land, and I owe no taxes to the British government. I built my house, barn, fences, and mill from my trees. We can't let the King take it away! Your sons and my sons will fight, and you and I will fight, too. We will protect what a gracious God and His Providence has given us. God tells us in the Holy Writ He is no friend to tyranny,"

James loudly proclaimed his sound belief in the right to fight for America's freedom.

*****

Only hot cake crumbs and scraps of bacon were left on the platters and plates on the table. The eggs had been scraped clean, as had the peach pie. Excitement, tinged with melancholy, had not hampered any appetites, except for Elizabeth's. She felt like her throat was sewn shut, but she continued to laugh and reminisce with her boys.

"Uncle James, do you recollect the day William gave me my pistol?" questioned Andy.

"Aye, you grinned like a possum for days!" replied James. "Did you clean your weapons to a fine shine last night? A soldier has to be able to defend himself at all times. Handy weapons are no good if they aren't clean and primed."

Robert poked Andy with his elbow.

"William is only four years older than me, and six years ahead of you. He has the rank of major and leads his own men. Can you believe we used to wrestle each other when he lived with his uncle, Reverend Richardson?"

"Egad, Andy, mayhap you and I will have our own militia in a few years!"

Robert's admiration for the young major was

evident in his voice.

As he reminisced, Andy vigorously nodded his head and showed off his possum grin once more.

"That William is sharp-witted for his age, too. I remember one day he throwed me in a wrestling match. I always make it a point to not stay throwed either.

"Before I could scramble up, he grabbed my arm and had me on my feet in seconds. He even pounded my back as if I was the winner.

"He didn't gloat or make fun of my loss or my size. William complimented my spunk to the crowd around us. I haven't forgotten that afternoon, and I admire him."

Elizabeth regarded both her sons and pondered their words. She had not known the respect her boys had for William.

Heroes were vital to young men, and her sons would have William as their leader. The young man had inherited 150 acres and his uncle's large library. He had worked hard in his studies at Princeton, graduating with honors. Elizabeth wished her sons had William's zeal as a scholar, but she was glad they admired his character.

Her son Hugh had been under his command at Stono Ferry. On several occasions, William reassured the mourning Elizabeth and her other two sons what a brave and fearless soldier her son had been. All three recognized the sincerity of William's words.

William had been wounded leading a charge at Stono Ferry, and his convalescence was long. She had heard that he had read for the law while his body healed. His new troop of cavalry was now organized and ready to defend the Upcountry. Robert and Andy Jackson were riding out with this militia leader today.

"Tis time to check your gear," James said, as he pointed toward the two piles on either side of the door.

Both boys strode toward their paraphernalia; the

equipment was standard for each militiamen. Elizabeth tossed the yellow scarf over Robert's shoulder, as he walked around her.

As she handed the blue one to Andy, she again choked back her intense emotions of apprehension. The considerations of losing another son to this brutal war for freedom were unthinkable; already this new world had greedily stolen her young husband and eldest boy. A cold shiver ran down her spine at the possibilities of more loss.

Elizabeth grabbed Andy's arm, turned him around, and pulled the large shirt out from his skinny torso.

"Methinks the seams will stay tight in your shirt, Andy. I triple stitched each one last night. With your growing spell in the spring, I made this new shirt out of last year's cotton."

She looked at the brown linen breeches both young men wore and was satisfied with her spinning and weaving. They should survive the grueling lifestyle of a soldier riding on the Indian trails and in camps. Both of their weskits, the short, buttoned vests, were natural hemp colors that would blend in as camouflage during the summer months.

Brown slouch hats and well-worn, leather moccasins would protect their heads and feet. Robert's skinny feet were longer than last year, and Elizabeth had put an extra pair of woolen socks in his haversack. She believed he would walk right out of at least one pair of socks, and she was well aware that neither of her sons was prone to mending.

"Uncle James, look how fine your knife carved the date lines of the notches in my powder horn," Robert proudly held it up for his uncle to see. "I carved 1780 under my name after I made the new plug. I will whittle the names of all the battles we fight in at night near the fire. I plan to have skirmish names encircling this powder horn by the time this war is over. Andy and I will do our duty and are proud to join the fight for liberty!"

Andy interrupted his brother, "Huzzzah!"

In seconds, all four voices cheered loudly together, "Huzzah! Huzzah! Huzzah!"

"Remember Tarleton's Quarter! Remember Bloody Ban!" screamed Robert in a shout that shook the rafters.

The Jackson boys would never forget the mangled bodies from the cruelty of the British at the Battle of Waxhaws. Images of those hacked limbs and bloody faces were etched in their memories. Just like in the hearts of other patriots in South Carolina, vengeance ruled since May 29 against their enemies. Evening the score was in the front of their minds.

Elizabeth watched the two pick up their equipment from the individual piles. First, they donned hunting shirts and belted them. Their neckcloths were tied, and the full haversacks were flung quickly over their necks. Besides food, the haversacks held tinderboxes with the flint and char cloth needed to start a fire. A small sewing kit with thread and wooden needles was in between the extra socks.

Next Robert and Andy picked up a larger tin box attached to a shoulder belt; it held thirty-six rolled and ready cartridges, layered four wide to protect them from the rain. New, handmade bullets made from Elizabeth's pewter plates were in leather pouches tied shut with cord.

Each son then picked up his ax, canteen, knife, powder horn, and wooden drinking cup. The axes and sheathed knives were tucked into their belts, and the canteens and cups were tied onto that same belt. The powder horn, tied to its own leather strap, was also tossed over their necks.

Smiling and nodding, the mother reached over to straighten straps and check on the tightness of cords on each new soldier. The flattening and smoothing of what needed no adjusting gave her moments to cherish their presence once again.

Elizabeth admired the Kentucky rifles that gleamed in the sunrise. The boys had polished the walnut wood, brass, and leather straps to a fine sheen. They were in the habit of cleaning their firearms daily, and she knew they would make every shot count.

Robert and Andy were proud of the long-barreled, slender stock rifles that James had bought for them when each turned twelve. This rite of passage into manhood was an honorable one, and each Scotch-Irish boy looked forward to his own day of recognition.

Angst and panic about possible future war nightmares and loss furrowed Elizabeth's brow. There was an art as certainly as there were laws to war, and her boys were going to study them as they lived it.

James noticed the dark clouds in Elizabeth's face, quickly stood up, and went to pick up his fiddle case.

"Aye, tis time to bring some song into this home. I see the sun rising in the east behind you, Elizabeth. You be supporting your sons to go fight against our enemy, and I know you will worry Heaven's Gate with prayers of protection around them. Let's sing a wee tune together now."

As the lonesome chords filled the room, one after another the family joined in the first verse of "Johnny Has Gone for a Soldier."

Here I sit on Beacon Hill, with salty eyes I cry my fill, And every tear would turn a mill, Johnny's gone for a soldier. Shule shule shule aroo, Shule shule shule aroo.

and every tear would turn a mill, Johnny's gone for a soldier.

With pipes and drums he marched away. He would not heed the words I did say. He'll not come back for many a day. Johnny's gone for a soldier Shule shule shule aroo, Shule shule shule He'll not come back for many a day, Johnny's gone for a soldier.

I'll sell my rod, I'll sell my reel, and likewise sell my grindin' wheel, To buy my Johnny a sword of steel, Johnny's gone for a soldier. Shule shule shule aroo, Shule shule shule arro, to buy my Johnny a sword of steel, Johnny's gone for a soldier.

I'll don my cloak of crimson red, and through this world I'll beg for my bread, I'll find my Johnny be him 'live or dead, Johnny 's gone for a soldier. Shule shule shule aroo, Shule shule shule I'll find my Johnny be him 'live or dead, Johnny's gone, my Johnny has gone, Johnny has gone for a soldier.

Elizabeth's lilting soprano voice meshed into the tenor and baritone voices of the men, as the family sang these popular lyrics about the price of war.

Capture and Jail
1781

Andy eagerly followed his idol, William Richardson Davie. The Major appointed Andy as a messenger, and the thirteen- year-old performed his task. Because he knew the trails and was an expert horseman for his age, Andy was suited for this assignment.

At Hanging Rock on August 6, 1780, Andy and Robert were in Davie's command under General Thomas Sumter. The Patriots defeated a large force of Tory regulars.

From this time until the next year of 1781, guerrilla warfare abounded in the Waxhaws. It was these quick and surprise raids that left both farmland and homes destroyed. Over and over, the Patriots left their homes for days at a time and fled north to Charlotte. When the British retired because of lack of food or insurgence in another section, the Jacksons, Crawfords, and their neighbors would return to salvage and recover what was left.

One day the family had to run once again into hiding in the woods after being warned by a messenger that the British Legion was on the move again up the Camden Road. Not knowing which course or home would be in their sights that morning, everyone dashed for cover.

Elizabeth left the planked bass cooking and hoped the smell of the baking fish would not fill the nostrils of any hungry soldiers. Time was of the essence, and none could be spared for picking up sentimental belongings. The family ran, as the messenger rode on to warn others.

Elizabeth crawled in between Robert and Andy under the low limbs of some scrub pines; all three rested their rifles in a ready position on a fallen log. One of the Crawford cousins lay beside Andy. They slowed their breathing and were quieter than the normal forest sounds. Anxiety permeated their bodies, but only their eyes darted from side-to- side.

Within a few minutes of arranging their rifles, the pounding of hooves assailed their ears. Elizabeth clutched her rifle to help control her beating heart trying to jump out of her chest. The needles and limbs started to shake above their heads, and then the first horses came into view.

The cavalry wore short green jackets with black roll collars. Their white breeches reached the black riding boots. On their heads sat black leather caps shaped like iron pots. Sabers and pistols were their armor.

Their faces were sternly focused on looking ahead. But no face was more severe than the leader. He sat straight in the saddle with a firm grip on the reins. His shoulders were stiff, and his expression harsh.

There was an unyielding control and proud look to his body language. A large bunch of black plumes was attached to the helmet of that British warrior, Banastre Tarleton.

Almost imperceptibly Robert reached across Elizabeth's back to touch Andy's shoulder. His other arm and handheld his rifle steady, and his eyes never left the road. Andy gave a half nod in return. What they witnessed at the Waxhaws battlefield roared instantly into their minds.

Only a hundred yards away from those hidden rode Bloody Ban!

Protection, not attack, had to be their recourse this day; firing would be chancy at this range. Andy's temper almost prevailed, as he watched the horse and rider move in and then out of the sights of his rifle. His trigger finger tightened, but he could not fire. Andy could not doom his mother to the reprisal of a prideful shot. Taking a slow, deep breath, the now fourteen- year-old held steady.

*****

Walking back toward their home, Elizabeth hastily scurried for the planked bass. She had soaked the cedar boards all night to be sure there was no chance of their catching on fire. Cooking outside could be dangerous if left unsupervised, and she needed to check on any popping embers. The fire had been built in a prepared spot. Elizabeth had swept and picked up all the leaves and twigs, and river stones circled the site. After Elizabeth filled the cavity of the fish with butter, thyme, salt, and ginger, she tightly secured the bass with her handmade cords onto the boards.

She saw how the scales were blackened on the sides closest to the coals. One by one she untied each fish, slathered it with butter, and generously poured vinegar over each bass. Then she pushed the planks back into the ground; their cooking was nigh complete.

As Elizabeth pondered what to serve with the bass, she realized little variety was left in the root cellar now. One small head of cabbage still hung from its roots. Two turnips and three small carrots, stuck individually in sand, still flourished as if in the ground. With some of the same seasoning that were also on the fish, cooking them together in an iron pot would be tasty with the fish. Elizabeth had picked wild pokeweed and dandelions yesterday, and the fresh greens would add more flavor. With hearth-cooking, much could be cooked in the same pot. A pone of cornmeal, slathered with the butter she made this morning, would help fill up her growing sons' stomachs once again.

Elizabeth's mother had called springtime "six

127

weeks of want." There was nothing up yet in the garden, and last year's supplies of vegetables and meat were skimpy. These spring days were all about using the bottom of the barrel, and Elizabeth was grateful that last year's harvests had been plentiful. Whether new crops would be either planted or harvested this year would depend on how many times armies from both sides made themselves welcome on James' property.

With the longer days and more daylight, the chickens had started laying eggs again. Tasting those fresh eggs was welcome to the whole family. Elizabeth wondered why the hens stopped laying in the fall each year. Contrary to any reasoning or questions she might have, she reckoned it was all about Providence.

For months now, they had fled their homes and land, as the enemy advanced. At a moment's notice, they would flee either to the woods, as today, or further north toward the homes of friends and family. Today's hiding out wasn't lengthy compared to others.

*****

The family gathered for the feast of baked fish and vegetables, and Elizabeth asked Robert to bless the meal. It was only the three of them, and the table looked and felt empty today.

Quizzically, Robert looked at Elizabeth before bowing his head.

"Andy and I like the meal blessing we heard in camp. We, fellows, took up saying it. I might could get attached to these words.

For the blessings you've bestowed upon this home and on this family,
For all the days we've had together and all the days to come,

*For the joys and sorrows that bind us ever closer, For
the trials we've overcome,
And for teaching us that we can do no great things,
Only small things with great love, Lord, we thank you.
Amen!*

"It's a wee long, brother," grinned Andy, "but it
covers a plenty."

More than they had eaten at one sitting for
months, the small family enjoyed each mouthful
Elizabeth had lovingly prepared.

Without saying a word, Robert and Andy
hunkered over their wooden plates and greedily cleaned
them. Elizabeth ate more slowly and left some food on
her plate for the one pig outside.

Food, animals, and people were now living in a
desert that had once been called a garden. The pillaging
and burning by both enemies and friends left little for
any of the refuges.

"This war has become ugly here in the
Waxhaws. Rather than armies fighting each other, there
are neighbors who have become enemies settling old
scores," pondered Robert.

"Aye," Elizabeth responded. "Men are hunting
other men for vengeance. Hangings are carried out at the
nearest trees without the benefit or luxury of trials."

She shivered as she thought of the stories of
ransacking homes and barns that were weekly
occurrences. Hungry children and wives drove men to
dastardly acts to stop the tears and crying because of
growling stomachs.

Andy's mouth changed to a straight line, and his
eyes darkened in dismay.

Softly he said, "Frank looked wild out of his
wide eyes when I saw him ride by last week. He
reminded me of that crazy coon last summer that jumped
at Robert; both were out of control. The animal was

furious at nothing and wobbled from side-to-side. Not realizing what he was doing, Frank savagely whipped his horse for more speed and almost fell off."

"I never heard tell before of someone going mad as a hatter over a sorrow happening to a friend," Elizabeth paused and looked up from her lap.

"In only four days, Frank hunted down and killed all twenty Tories who murdered and mutilated his neighbor. 'Twas only after he killed the last man that Frank came back to his real self.

War does severe damage to a man's mind and heart. Its ugliness spreads like poison, and antidotes aren't always effective."

She shook her head at the visions of what war demanded and took from its soldiers.

Sensing her worries about her sons, Robert reached over to Elizabeth to encourage her. He patted her hand and then rose to give her a whopping hug. Andy sprang up and bounded over to Elizabeth, too. From both sides, the young men squashed their mother between them. Laughter filled the room, and Elizabeth's solemn face sparkled with glee.

The three then grabbed hands and danced a jig around the room.

Spontaneously, Elizabeth started to sing the childhood round of "Rattlin' Bog." The wildlife outside quickly became silent because of the din inside the Crawford home.

*****

On April 10, 1781, Lord Francis Rawdon sent Colonel John Coffin and a company of 150 soldiers from Camden to the Waxhaws to rally the Tories with destructive and neutralizing attacks on the area Whigs. Coffin's troops included experienced light dragoons,

130

infantry, and Tories.

Robert and Andy had joined the command of Major Robert Crawford, the brother of their Uncle James. When word reached the Patriots of this force, they assembled at the Waxhaws Meeting House, their regular muster ground. By the time the British regulars arrived, there were around forty Whigs finally assembled at their rendezvous point in a grove next to the building.

Armed and eager to defend their turf once again, the Whig militia met their Tory counterparts. Both sides similarly dressed in hunter's garb; both sides Americans, valiantly assured they were in the right.

Within minutes, behind the Tory militia, the uniformed dragoons and their galloping horses rode into the scene. Sabers held high in the air, their blood-curdling shouts were as intimidating as their appearance. Completely deceived by this unexpected force, the Whigs fought bravely, but sheer numbers soon prevailed in their defeat.

Eleven Patriots were captured at once, but the rest escaped on horseback with the dragoons in fierce pursuit. First, hurtling down the road and then across a field, the flight then careened into a marsh. Horses from both sides lost their footing in the quagmire, but more Patriots escaped their pursuers. Familiarity with their own marshland gave them the upper hand over the British trackers.

It was a night of mayhem as the British first burned the Waxhaws Meeting House; then they set their sights on neighboring farms and homes. They randomly attacked and burned houses, occupied or not. Stolen horses were tethered and led away. Soldiers plundered at will whatever took their fancy. There was no mercy given to the already struggling families who had little to lose.

James Crawford's home, where Elizabeth stood

alone behind a barred door with her rifle primed and ready, was spared. The mother heard the firing and the horses galloping in various directions. Shouts of mockery and disdain filled the air, and then she smelled the common odor of burning wood. Knowing it was not a cook fire this time of night, Elizabeth carefully cracked the shuttered window to stare at soaring flames and dense smoke in several directions from the house. The inferno mocked her safety behind locked doors and windows.

She was not afraid for herself: it was her sons' well-being that caused her heart to beat audibly. The friends of liberty were being hunted like forest animals, and no one was safe. Knowing Robert and Andy had joined the other volunteers at the meeting house, she could only hope and pray that they were safe.

As Elizabeth guarded the homestead, her two sons were riding for their lives.

Robert and Andy became separated, but Andy and his cousin Thomas Crawford rode side-by-side through the mud and shallow water. Andy's horse was first to stand on firm land, and he looked back to check on his cousin's progress.

"No! No!" Andy hollered. "Get up, Thomas! Run!"

Thomas' horse had mis-stepped and fallen sideways in the mire. Before the rider could stand and run, a British saber hit his head. With fire in his eyes, the cavalryman lifted the heavy sword once again but recognized the fight was over. The dazed Thomas struggled to his feet to escape, but the blow had disoriented him. Slowly he raised his hands above his head in surrender and motioned Andy to ride on, as more British soldiers arrived on the scene. In frustration and anger at his inability to help Thomas, Andy jerked his mount's reins toward the top of the slope and headed for the woods.

The young man furiously gritted his teeth at the scene of his cousin surrounded by those green and red jackets. Leaving Thomas behind went against the grain. Startled by the sight of another horseman out of the corner of his eye, Andy recognized Robert's green farmer's hat with the turkey feather. They excitedly waved at each other and rode toward a narrow trail that led to the creek.

Not speaking until they reached a secret bend in the creek, the brothers jumped off their horses and tied them to some low branches. Scooting under an overhanging rock, they took deep breaths and were finally able to talk.

"Ye appear to be one of those ragamuffins Mother used to accuse ye of being!" Robert poked his brother in the rib.

"Aye," quickly replied Andy. "I reckon we are a pair. I think it fitting we rest a spell."

The fourteen and sixteen-year-old stayed vigilant, but quiet on the bank of Cain Creek.

Sunrise broke within a few hours, and the exhausted boys saw its first rays. Surviving the night, Robert and Andy were famished. The closest home for begging victuals was Thomas's home. Andy felt a need to tell his wife about her husband's bravery at the hands of his British attacker.

Stiff and discomfited from their naps, they stretched their muscles in their shoulders, arms, and legs as they walked to limber up. Their horses were well-fed from sprigs of grass and the pea vines surrounding them and ready for a morning ride.

Arriving at the outskirts of Thomas' property, all appeared in order. There were no British sentries in place, and the dogs were napping in the front yard. Stealthily walking across the garden plot, Robert walked in the door in front of Andy. They both carried their rifles at the ready and scanned the room through the sights.

The home scene welcomed them with smells of breakfast. They placed their rifles beside the door and entered with worn-out smiles.Soon fried eggs and potatoes were placed in front of them.

Suddenly enemy troops burst into the keeping room. Thomas's wife grabbed the baby close to her heart, as the British soldiers turned over the trestle table breaking dishes and crockery and tearing up clothes and bedding. Overcome by the surprise and the numbers, the inside of the Crawford home was wrecked, as it was turned upside down.

Last into the home was the Major John Coffin, a swaggering young man who was pleased with the shattered lives he saw before him. Their sojourn into the Waxhaws surely had not only destroyed buildings, taken prisoners and booty, but he was sure the Patriot's moral was crushed.

While his men looted the house, the arrogant officer walked over to where Andy stood with his anger barely in check. He pointed his quirt in Andy's face and gave an egotistical order, "Kneel, and polish my muddy boots, boy."

The order was a personal affront, and Andy's response was tautly his own.

"Sir, I am a prisoner of war and claim to be treated as such," he said through clenched teeth.

In anger and disbelief, the officer raised his sword and swung at Andy's head, obviously seeking to cut off his head. Raising his left arm, Andy averted the killing blow. Screaming in pain, Andy's left hand and head sprayed blood from the slashes.

The officer didn't hesitate but immediately turned to Robert with the same insane request of cleaning his boots. When Robert also defied the order, he reeled across the room from the passionate blow he received from the officer's sword. Robert then lay still.

As if the boys' insubordination had bothered him not, the officer turned, wiped off his sword, and walked out the door without a further look at the bedlam.

Robert and Andy's hands were tied behind their backs, and they were led outside to join the rest of the Waxhaws' prisoners, including Thomas. Their wounds were ignored. The British and Tories made sure they helped their new prisoners fall into line with much unnecessary punching and pushing. A deep-seated derision for their enemies was obvious.

As the twenty prisoners, including Thomas, marched past the fence around the Crawford house, Robert and Andy saw their mother. The three pairs of eyes were glued on each other until sight was impossible.

Elizabeth continued to wave her hand backward as she had always done. Rather than waving good-by with the palm toward those leaving her home, Elizabeth waved a "come here" to invite all back.

The Camden Gaol
1781

Elizabeth noted the chickens had all the seeds and grains they could forage in the yard, and her one remaining cow still grazed in the field where dozens of cows and James' prize bulls used to daily eat.

It had only been a few weeks since James had died from a bullet he took in a skirmish. There were red streaks moving up and down his leg from the wound by the time he was brought home. The bone was shattered, and the tendons visible. The skin was filthy around the mangled flesh. Elizabeth first poured honey over the fiery hole and then saturated the site with a yarrow poultice.

Despite all the remedies that Elizabeth tried, the injury continued to fester. James finally lost consciousness and died in his sleep.

Elizabeth realized her face was wet from tears at the thoughts of losing James. He was a kind man who lived life with an open hand.

When he had invited her to join his household, she had two boys and was expecting a third. At that time, she only had a glimpse of his generous spirit. He worked mighty hard to make a living in this new world for his family, and he prospered. James was a caring father-figure to her children when they were young, but he challenged them to be strong men of character as they grew older.

Shaking her head at the number of deaths in her family she had suffered, she fell on the ground in a heap. Elizabeth pounded the hard clay in frustration and anger at the losses of her loved ones.

Overwhelmed with the new reality of Robert and Andy being captured by the British was too much to bear. She furiously pulled up clumps of grass and threw them helter-skelter with all of her might. Finally, her anguish subsided to moans, and then she lay still, momentarily drained of her despair.

Besides the sounds of her loss of hope, over and over she said her son's names, as only a mother speaks the names of her children.

"Hugh, Robert. Andy! Hugh, Robert, Andy!"

*****

After two days of the forced march, without food or water, Robert, Andy, and the other eighteen prisoners were weak and exhausted. This inhumane treatment was inexcusable, but the commanding officer, Major John Coffin, had already shown his lack of honor at the Waxhaws.

Dried, as well as oozing blood, stained the brothers' faces, necks, and shirts. Around Robert's head was wound his yellow scarf that now resembled a rag. Andy had wrapped his torn indigo scarf around his left hand, but the wound continued to seep blood every time he moved.

The brothers stayed close together on the forty-mile march. Trudging turned to stumbling; their arms around each other's shoulders stabilized their staggering steps.

It was dusk when the prisoners of war arrived at the Camden District Jail. Designed and built like others in the colony, the wooden structure was three stories high. A dungeon and garret used as a public room completed the imposing rectangular edifice.

As the shoving continued by their guards, the prisoners walked around the earth redoubt, a mound piled high with dirt, and a palisade log fence that protected the prison. The brothers viewed the fortifications with dismay, when they viewed the six-pound gun mounted on a platform. After they crossed the defensive moat that would slow any enemy troops, the men walked around an oval abatis; this barrier was filled with pointed and jagged brushwood and trees. The overcrowded jail held 250 prisoners.

One of their guards intentionally pushed Thomas into the sharp branches that faced outward from that last barricade. Laughter and jeers followed Thomas' shrill cries of pain. Andy moved toward his cousin but was blocked by a sneering Tory.

Surviving the pain, both physical and mental, inflicted by the guards was a test of endurance. The line of prisoners walked up the wooden staircase to the second floor, where the cells were. At the top of the stairs, the men were ordered to take off their shoes and coats.

Robert, along with two of the other Waxhaws men, was pushed into the first door of a crammed cell. Andy made to follow but was stopped with a bayonet to his chest.

The soldier scoffed, "Nay, boy, ye be down the hall aways. Rules are that family is separated. All prisoners are scheduled for the hangman, so ye will meet again at the Pearly Gates or mayhap Hell's Gates."

Robert nodded to his brother, and Andy moved on down the hall, as commanded, to another crowded cell.

There were no beds in the confined spaces, so the prisoners stood, sat, or lay down as they could. A small, barred window let little light in, so the shadows added to the gloom.

One man, lying in the corner and suffering from the pox, raised his head at the intrusion.

"Help me, man!" his weak voice cried. "My body is afire, and it aches like I have taken a beating.

Look at me!"

Andy looked in pity at the man's misfortune, but then he realized that most of the strangers in the cell were either suffering from some stage of smallpox or had pulled through from the dreaded illness. Scars pitted some of the prisoner's faces; although the sores had faded. Dirty rags were wrapped around the eyes of three men; the illness took their eyesight.

Without warning, his body shivered and started to shake at what lay ahead of him. Andy slumped to the floor and leaned against the firm bars of the cell. The guard slammed and locked the iron door and swaggered away.

The daily schedule never varied. With catcalls and sneers, the guards delivered stale bread each morning and pitched it into each cell. After eating, those that could move walked in place and stretched their arms. This paltry exercise easily wore them out, and naps were next on the agenda. Another exercise interval ended the daylight hours before they swapped stories. Only amusing tales were countenanced and expected. When dusk fell, the inmates sang the ballads and hymns learned in childhood until the guards called for silence. Silence was demanded early each evening until morning light.

Intimidation and terror were the rules that governed Camden Gaol.

Trying to tend to their comrades was difficult without doctors, medicines, or extra blankets. Encouragement to not give up and fight the infectious disease that seemed to randomly jump from one man to another was little balm to those suffering.

Within three days after Robert and Andy were captured, Elizabeth borrowed two horses to make the trip to Camden. As were all the animals in the Waxhaws, the old and scraggy mounts were past their prime. With two armies scouring the Waxhaws for supplies for almost a year, the best animal stock was long gone. Elizabeth had been to several farms to find even the two she had, but her neighbors were willing to help the single mother in her quest. Before more catastrophes befell her sons, Elizabeth meant to negotiate for her son's release. She was not a woman to stand by when there was a task to be accomplished.

Praying for guidance as she rode, forty-year-old Elizabeth chose to keep a steady pace with the horses. Galloping might cause more harm to their physical condition, and she would need them fairly fit to get herself and her sons back home.

She carried a poke of dry clothes and a few potatoes with her. Before she left that morning, she baked corn cakes with only water, cornmeal, and one egg; the twelve small cakes were wrapped in her pockets. Knowing that nourishment was what her sons would need most, she wanted to give them something cooked in her kitchen.

Before the war, Elizabeth had traveled with James to the store owned by Joseph Kershaw. He was a generous man, and now she would seek his advice on getting her sons released. Because of his leadership in the community as businessman and Sheriff, Mr. Kershaw would be able to tell her whom to talk to and how to proceed.

Around noon of the second day, Elizabeth arrived in Camden. She quickly found out that Joseph Kershaw had been imprisoned after the Battle of Camden and banished to Bermuda. At first, she was at a loss on what to do next, and then Elizabeth literally ran into a young boy who gave her the information she needed.

He was whistling the Irish tune, "Rattlin' Bog," so Elizabeth stopped him and quietly asked. "Lad, prithee where might I find a Patriot militiaman?"

Elizabeth encouraged his honest answer with a smile and a nod.

Looking around him before he spoke, the scrawny and barefoot boy motioned to the left. "Two streets over at the house with roses alongside the door," he whispered, as he kept on walking.

Arriving at the one- room house, Elizabeth spoke quickly to the militia captain who answered her knock with a loaded pistol in his hand. Neither tarried in their conversation, and he told Elizabeth that negotiations were under way for a prisoner exchange.

Elizabeth determined that she needed to speak to the man who would sign the releases,

Lord Rawdon. The twenty-six- year-old Lieutenant Colonel Francis Rawdon was the commander of the Volunteers of Ireland and the prison in Camden. He was haughty and proud of his connection and rapport with Earl Cornwallis.

Rawdon's orderly interrupted his superior with care with a quiet knock at the office door. A brusque voice replied, "Enter."

"Sir, I beg pardon, sir, to disturb you this bonny fine morning," the young man paused to determine whether he would be granted permission to continue.

Lord Rawdon chose not to look up from the paper he was reading, but he gave a brief nod of assent that he was listening.

"Sir, an Irish mother appeals to His Grace to come before him to petition him for the release of her sons."

Rawdon slowly raised his head to look at his aid. He lifted his eyebrows and turned his mouth up in apparent unconcern and lack of forbearance.

"A pox on my ever finishing my work by midday! My office hours are not my own betwixt interruptions and these provincials seeking favors. There is usually neither rhyme nor reason behind their requests, even though they plead so earnestly. Send her in!"

Elizabeth had heard Lord Rawdon's rant; he had not attempted to speak softly.

In her worn and patched skirt and bodice, she straightened her neckerchief and tucked her hair back under her cap as she walked through the door. Her face was calm, but her heart beat furiously in her chest.

The Irish nobleman who awaited her was dressed in his full uniform and wore all his ribbons and medals. He had received congratulations on his defeat of Major General Nathanael Greene at Hobkirk's Hill on April 25. Rawdon had audaciously attacked and defeated the superior Patriot force, and his pride and arrogance were apparent, even down to his hands laid purposely flat on the desk.

"My Lord, I beseech your pardon for my two sons, Robert and Andy Jackson. Word has it that a prisoner exchange is being discussed, and I beg you to add their names to the list. The youngest has only turned fourteen, and Robert is sixteen. I will take responsibility for their future actions," spoke the seemingly composed, though bedraggled, mother.

Her lilting Irish accent caught Lord Rawson unawares. Yes, the men in his regiment from Ireland still spoke with their Irish brogue, but the soft and feminine inflections of Elizabeth's speech obliged him to think of home and his family.

Rawdon did not immediately reply. Looking through the stack of papers on his desk, Rawdon found the list he sought. It was this morning's registry of those prisoners afflicted with smallpox. Quickly scanning the record, he saw both Robert and Andy Jackson's names.

A glint in his eye appeared, as he thought how to

satisfy the Patriot mother and also protect his men. Allowing the exchange of these sick boys would take the dreaded disease to their home and community and also rid his prison of two with the revolting disease.

Looking up into Elizabeth's expectant eyes, Rawdon finally answered the silent mother.

"It appears that both your sons have contracted smallpox. I believe it will be best for them to be part of our trade for prisoners. You may pick them up tomorrow."

Lord Rawdon stood and walked toward the window where sunlight streaked into his office. With his hands folded behind his back, he turned back to Elizabeth and his office. There was no kindness or sympathy in his look, only exasperation at being disturbed.

*****

The next morning Elizabeth arrived at the prison gates by sunrise. It was pouring rain, and a chill was in the wind.

Two barefoot scarecrows lurched out of the gates. The taller one was supported by the other, and Robert's face was marked by the smallpox sores. His eyes were glazed with fever; he would have toppled over if Andy hadn't supported him. Andy pushed his brother onto the horse's saddle and then greeted his mother.

"Ye are a sight for sore eyes, Mamma. I don't want to tarry; I want to go home!"

"My son, I praise God that I am seeing your dear face and your brother's! I fear we must ride quickly, because there is more safety at home. We will talk later.

"Can you ride double with Robert?" questioned Elizabeth. This had been her plan from the beginning, but now she was unsure about the strength of the old

143

horses.

"Robert is too weak to guide the horse; he needs me to walk ahead and lead the animal. I mean to help him all I can."

Elizabeth grabbed both of Andy's hands in her own and covered them with kisses. Andy chuckled, "Mamma, mayhap someone will see you.

They will think you are crazy as a bedbug!"

Releasing his hands, Elizabeth laughed herself and pulled the horse's reins. Those forty miles home in this rain would be a challenge. Elizabeth believed they were going to need some laughter on this trip. As the Good Book said, "A merry heart doeth good, like medicine." She resolved to bring more laughter into their home; a flood of sadness had overwhelmed it.

By the time they arrived to their Waxhaws home, Robert was either delirious or in a coma. Andy now had chills and open sores. Elizabeth put them to bed on pallets close to the fireplace in the keeping room.

Tending them consumed both her days and nights. Elizabeth covered and recovered their gaunt bodies when they kicked the blankets off in their fevered delirium. The cool cloths she tenderly placed on their foreheads rapidly turned warm and had to be swapped. She spooned nourishing potato soup and chicken broth into their mouths, one teaspoon at a time. Sometimes the cold well water soothed their parched lips and throat, and at other times the sick boys would spit it out. She sang to them, read to them, and prayed aloud for them.

As Andy continued to talk nonsense, Robert's body became quieter, and he slept more and more. Elizabeth sat between her two sons on the floor and sometimes cradled them in her arms as she had when they were younger. Over and over, she told them how much she loved them and how proud she was of them. She shared with them her memories of the early married

144

life with their father.

Each family story brought back vivid reminisces of happier days. Even if they didn't respond to her voice, Elizabeth believed they heard her. Robert finally lost the battle with smallpox and died. In his delirium, Andy didn't realize it.

After burying Robert next to his father in the Waxhaws Meeting House cemetery, Elizabeth focused all her energy on her one son who still survived. Malaria attacked his weakened body next as he was recuperating from smallpox. Again, the boy and his mother fought the onslaught of more chills and fever.

It was into the warm summer month of June before Andy's strength came back. His fun-loving spirit once more brightened the family home. His many freckles that had disappeared in the sickly pallor of his complexion blotched his face with a few scars from the smallpox. Visitors were challenged to arm wrestling by the patient, and Elizabeth had difficulty keeping his hunger at bay.

She worked hard in the spring garden, finding old seeds and replanting them. The Waxhaws community shared what they had with each other, so no one was in grave want. Potatoes once again were served at every meal, and the women searched the woods for edible greens. Green leaves and stalks were above ground about two feet in the cornfield, so it was promising. Even the orchard had small peaches, and both Elizabeth and Andrew hankered for a pie.

The British were in retreat toward Charlestown, so they were not as consumed with the defense of their area as they had been in the spring. Andy started repairing fences and slowly rebuilt the barn. The rocks had to be replaced around the well, so river rocks were needed. All the buildings were in poor condition or completely wrecked.

A large part of the flax field survived, and the blue flowers once more brightened that plot of land. She had found all the pieces of her loom and spinning wheel, and Andrew was steadily putting both back together. Elizabeth was excited about the cloth she would weave this fall and winter. There were patches on top of patches on their few pieces of clothing now. Andy had named them the Scarecrow Jacksons, and it was apt.

Starting over was the only course of action. Life as they knew it had been wrecked by the British sojourn in the Waxhaws.

For Sunday lunch in July, they were invited to Robert Crawford's. There they heard the news that James and Jane's sons had been captured and were on prison ships in the harbor of Charlestown. Orphaned now, Elizabeth was horrified that her nephews had no one to help them survive the death traps of those ships.

For several days, Elizabeth mulled over this new catastrophe to her family. She finally decided that Andy was strong enough to be left on his own. His Uncle James had taught him well what needed to be accomplished for a farm to prosper. The exercise would make his body stronger. Her quandary was in leaving her only son, and so Elizabeth decided to talk to Andy about what she might do. She knew Robert Crawford would see to his needs.

Andy had been thinking about his cousins on those prison ships, too, and he well knew how they were being treated by the British. When Elizabeth brought the conversation that evening around to her possible plans, Andy did not hesitate.

"Aye, Mamma, ye must go help them," he started to speak, but then had to stop.

The memories of what he and Robert endured in Camden rushed back into vivid color in his mind. He looked down at the spoon he was whittling out, then spoke again.

"If ye had not come to get me, I would be dead now! Mamma, I prithee go and bring my cousins back."

Mother and son talked about their family late into that night. He wanted to know more about the father he was named for. And he wanted to hear more about Ireland, his parents' birthplace. Andy even cautiously revealed some of his boyhood pranks with Elizabeth, thinking she knew nothing about them. It was late before the fire was banked for the night.

Five days later, Elizabeth, her friend Nancy, and two other women from the Waxhaws prepared to ride the two hundred miles to Charlestown. The women, as well as their families, had gathered in the Crawford yard to say their goodbyes.

Elizabeth put both her hands on Andy's shoulders, and her green eyes, glistening from unshed tears, shone with her love for him. Her voice was serious-minded, but kind.

"Andrew, if I should not see you again, I wish you to remember and treasure up some things I have already said to you.

"In this world, it is best to be self-sufficient, but never forsake your dependable friends. This war has taken too much of our family; there may come a day you need help of a stranger as so many have needed help from us. "

"You can make friends by being honest, and you can keep them by being loyal. Those friends will expect you to be trustworthy, too."

Elizabeth's voice cracked. She stopped and smiled at him.

Many thoughts had kept Elizabeth awake the night before. Reminders were all she had to share with Andy; there was nothing new to be said.

Andy had learned much from the world of war

this past year. School and texts were not the only way to gather an education that would serve best in the long run.

"In personal conduct always be courteous. I have seen that temper of yours overcome your sound judgment."

Elizabeth tightened her grip on Andy's shoulders; she wanted him to understand the importance of her next words.

"No one likes a bully, Andy. If your sabre scars remind you of that..." She reached out and gently touched the bright line on Andy's face. "Then you will always be the honorable and compassionate man I have watched you become."

Andy barely nodded his head in agreement.

Elizabeth tousled his red hair, almost the hue of her own.

"I love you, Andy, and I am most proud of the man you are and the man you are becoming."

Mother and son hugged. Elizabeth broke their embrace first with one last tightening of her arms around Andy. Then she turned and walked away to mount the horse that would take her to Charlestown.

The group of women cantered their horses toward the bend in the road where, for years, the Crawfords and Jacksons had watched friends and family disappear from view.

Elizabeth turned in her saddle once more and waved to her son, Andrew Jackson, future President of the United States of America.

Epilogue

Elizabeth Jackson arrived safely in Charleston. Along with the other women, intent on their mission of mercy, she received permission to nurse the sick and wounded on the prison ships.

Those captive Patriots, afflicted as much by disease as by their poorly healing injuries, rested on filthy floors below deck. Seldom granted time on deck during daylight hours, they spent most of their time in the bowels of the ships. Wormy bread and uncooked food were the daily rations. Both the sick and the emaciated groaned with their sufferings day and night.

It wasn't long before Elizabeth contracted cholera from one of the prisoners of war. Although it has now been nearly eradicated by modern science and hygiene, in the eighteenth century, prison ships provided a perfect breeding ground when germs were not understood and were just being discovered. Cholera quickly and viciously attacked the digestive tracks of many. In extreme cases, this disease killed within hours of its first systems.

No details are available on how long Elizabeth suffered with cholera. She died at the home of William and Agnes Barton. It is said that Mr. Barton built her coffin, and Mrs. Barton dressed Elizabeth's body in her own best outfit for burial.

In a letter to George Witherspoon dated August 11, 1824, Andrew Jackson writes, *I knew she [my mother] died near Charleston, having visited that City with several matrons to afford relief to our prisoners with the British – not her son as you suppose, for at that time my two Elder brothers were no more; but two of her Nephews, William and Joseph Crawford Sons of James Crawford then deceased. I well recollect one of the matrons that went with her was Mrs. Boyd. It is possible*

Mrs. Barton can inform me where she was buried that I can find her grave. This to me would be great satisfaction, that I might collect her bones and inter them with that of my father and brothers.

Elizabeth's unmarked grave has never been found. In a letter from George Witherspoon of Lancaster to her famous son, he wrote about her burial. "Your mother is buried in the suburbs of Charleston about one mile from what was then called the Governor's Gate, which is in and about the forks of Meeting and Kingstreet Roads."

A marker in her memory was placed in downtown Charleston in the middle of the College of Charleston campus. On this marker is one of the lines from her words of advice to her youngest son. "Andy, never tell a lie nor take what is not your own nor sue for slander. Settle those cases yourself."

The final version of this book contains a longer version of her words that concludes this historical fiction of her life.

Even though there is an unresolved mystery to where Elizabeth was buried in Charleston, we do know that Andrew Jackson received a small bundle of her belongings and word of her death in November, 1781. Taking medicine and supplies to two of her nephews on the British ships was her final merciful act. She, of course, would have tended all of the Patriots if she had the power to do so: Elizabeth was not self-centered, but generous of spirit.

I admire Elizabeth Jackson, sometimes called Betty by her family, She was a fearless woman who lived a life beholden to no one; she forged her own path. Despite a hardscrabble existence during both the Colonial and Revolutionary War years in our state, she persisted in doing the right thing and refused to be undone by tough circumstances. She earned her own living by weaving and saw to it that her three sons inherited their father's property. Obviously independent, she taught this by example to her sons.

Little documentation is available about Elizabeth Jackson's life. The sparseness of details led my creativity to include possible visits from Marquis de Lafayette and T. Bagge to the Crawford home. These famous men traveled through South Carolina at the proposed times, and their biographical information, as well as the description of Moravian culture, is accurate. The family's proximity to the Camden-Salisbury Road probably brought many unexpected visitors to the Caldwell door during these years and gave the family a reputation for hospitality.

Her stalwart character shines through in spite of the few facts. She bravely left her home and parents to travel across the Atlantic Ocean to join her sisters in the backwoods region of South Carolina. And she walked up that gangplank with an infant in her arms and a two-year-old by the hand.

After her husband's death, she raised her three sons as a single mother in the household of her ailing sister and her brother-in-law. Her extended family became her own. As with other Scots-Irish, the bonds of family were significant and vital. Never marrying again, she took on the household duties her sister was too weak to handle.

All the women of this Revolutionary War period needed to have nursing and medical skills because of the lack of doctors. Elizabeth intentionally sought opportunities to tend the sick, as is known by her presence at Buford's Massacre.

Her altruism and passionate love of liberty stirred her to play a pivotal role as a new nation was being born, and the cost required of her was definitive. Not only did this heroine bravely give up every worldly possession, subject herself to various forms of humiliation, and finally pay her last full measure for the cause of freedom, Elizabeth sent off all three of her sons to war.

Elizabeth was a woman of great actions and great love for her family, her country, and her God. She sought hope in the scriptures and encouraged her sons to have a deep-seated and unwavering faith in God, as well. She even thought that Andy, because of his intelligence, would make an effective Presbyterian minister. (Of course, she never knew that he would be elected President of the United States).

At age 14, Andy became an orphan and lived with his relatives. He carried his hatred of the British and the scars they gave him on his hand and head for the rest of his life. Learning as a young man from his mentor, William Richardson Davie, about war tactics during the Revolutionary War, he became a hero at the Battle of New Orleans.

His war experience, his mother's perseverance, and his time spent scrapping through the South Carolina wilderness helped steel Andy for the personal and political conflicts that followed him the rest of his life. The experiences of his family's early struggles to make ends meet stayed with him. Thriftiness was in his blood.

Elected the seventh President of the United States, Andy was our first President who had no formal education, though he became a lawyer, judge, and politician. Old Hickory, named because a hickory tree is tough, was the "people's President," and I believe his mother would have been proud.

As Thomas Paine wrote, "These are the times that try men's souls. The summer soldier and the sunshine patriot will, in this crisis, shrink from the service of their county; but he that stands it now, deserves the love and thanks of man and woman.

Tyranny like hell is not easily conquered yet we have this consolation with us, the harder the conflict, the more glorious the triumph. What we obtain too cheap, we esteem too lightly; it is dearness only that gives everything its value."

Elizabeth Jackson, the mother of President Andrew Jackson, who did not "shrink from the service of their [her] country...deserves the love and thanks of man and woman."

Bibliography

Bass, Robert D. *Ninety-Six, the Struggle for the S.C. Back Country*. Orangeburg, S.C.: The Sandlapper Store, Inc., 1978.

Booream, Hendrik. *Young Hickory: The Making of Andrew Jackson*. New York: Taylor Trade Publishers, 2001.

Borick, Carl P. A *Gallant Defense: The Siege of Charleston, 1780*. Columbia, S.C.: University of South Carolina Press, 2003.

Bray, Robert, and Paul Bushell, eds. *Diary of a Common Soldier in the American Revolution*. Dekalb, Illinois: Northern Illinois University Press, 1977.

Buchanan, John. *Jackson's Way*. New Jersey: John Wiley and Sons, Inc., 2001.

Buchanan, John. *The Road to Guilford Courthouse*. New Jersey: John Wiley and Sons, Inc., 1997.

Davis, Burke. *Old Hickory: A Life of Andrew Jackson*. New York: Dial Press, 1977.

Ellet, Elizabeth. *The Women of the American Revolution. Vol. 1*. New York: Baker and Scribner, 1848.

Floyd, Viola Caston. *Historical Notes from Lancaster County, S. C.*: Lancaster: Lancaster County Historical Commission, 1977.

Fries, Adelaide L. *Records of the Moravians in N.C.* Raleigh, N.C.: Litho Industries, 1968.

Fries, Adelaide L. *Road to Salem*. Winston-Salem, N.C.: John F. Blair, 1993.

Gullan, Harold. *Faith of Our Mothers*. Grand Rapids, Michigan: William B.Eerdman's Publishing Co., 2001.

Howe, George. *History of the Presbyterian Church in S.C. Vol. 1*. Columbia, S.C.: Duffie and Chapman, 1870.

James, Hunter. *Quiet People of the Land*. Chapel Hill, N.C.. University of North Carolina Press, 1976.

James, Marquis. *The Life of Andrew Jackson*. New York: The Bobbs- Merrill Co., 1933.

Johnson, Gerald W. *Andrew Jackson: An Epic in Homepun*. New York: Menton, 1927.

Lathn, Reverend Robert. *Historical Sketches of the Revolutionary War in the Upcountry of S.C.* Norfolk, Virginia: Broad River Basin Historical Society, 1984.

Lewis, Kenneth E. *The Camden Jail and Market Sites: A Report on Preliminary Investigations*. 1984.

Lumpkin, Henry. *From Savannah to Yorktown*. Lincoln, Nebraska: Excel Press, 1987.

Moore, Peter N. *World of Toil and Stress.*
Columbia, S.C.: University of S.C. Press,
2008.

Pettus, Louise. *The Nation Ford
Road.* Columbia, S.C.: Palmetton
Conservation Foundation, 2000.

Pettus, Louise, and Nancy Crockett. *Waxhaws.*
Rock Hill, SC.: Regal Graphics, 1993. Remini,

Robert V. *Andrew Jackson: Border
Captain.* Westport, Connecticut: Mecklin,
1990.

Schattschneider, Allen W. *Through Five Hundred
Years.* Winston- Salem, N.C.: Comenius
Press, 1982.

Shaw, Ronald E. *Andrew Jackson, 1767-1845.*
Dobbs Ferry, N. Y.: Oceana Publications, 1969.

Stanley, George Edward. *Andrew Jackson: Young
Patriot.* New York: Alladin Paperbacks, 2008.

Unger, Harlow Giles. *Lafayette.* New Jersey: John
Wiley and Sons, 2002.

Acknowledgements

"Let us dare to read, think, speak and write." – John Adams

Harvard graduate President John Adams was a philosopher and leader in the fight for liberty during the Revolutionary War. When the PBS series, John Adams, was shown again this July 4, 2013, I literally was glued to the television screen, watching America's history come alive once again. Yes, I have fallen in love with the men and women who sacrificed all to break free of England.

It is the people that give life to the facts. The word itself, "his story," revolves around the personal stories of people. Here in our state, from the coast to the upcountry, families fought in their own back yards and homes to withstand tyranny. More battles and skirmishes were fought in South Carolina than in any other colony, so the sketchy narratives are many. I applaud their perseverance and valor; without them, I would have no heroines and heroes to write about or learn from.

My development editor, Clare Neely, and my agent, Merianna Harrelson, have reassured and urged me on. Thank you, Dr. Christine Swager, for checking the text for historical accuracy. My family and friends anchored my progress by asking for an account of how many chapters were completed. Both the Daughters of the American Revolution and the Sons of the American Revolution, as well as book clubs, bookstores, and teachers have kindly asked for more biographical chronicles of our state.

Our son Scott has consistently made good suggestions that helped me clarify my thoughts, choose a better word, or throw out unnecessary verbiage. Thank you kindly for listening to my reading of the same paragraph countless times and agreeing that one word "fitly spoken" can transform a thought.

John and I celebrate thirty-four years of marriage in November of this year, so my dedication is to my husband John on our third book together. We have seen dreams become reality.

Sheila is the author of *Courageous Kate* and *Fearless Martha*. The National Society of the Daughters of the American Revolution presented Sheila with the Historic Preservation Award for "preserving the history of a South Carolina Heroine, Kate Barry, with her children's book for all ages." Sheila and her husband John live in Spartanburg, SC.